A Survey of Astronomy

A SERIES EDITED BY COLIN A. RONAN
ASSOCIATE EDITOR: PATRICK MOORE

There are already many excellent books upon elementary astronomy, and many technical works aimed purely at the expert. Books which form a connecting link between these two standards are rare. In general, the student finds that he has to pass straight from a very elementary volume on to a work which is of a high standard technically, and includes copious mathematical formulae.

The aim of the present series is to fill this gap in the literature. Some elementary knowledge has been assumed, but the general reader with no specialized knowledge will be able to follow the text, since mathematical formulae have been used sparingly and, in general, in footnotes or appendices. Some volumes necessarily make more use of mathematics than others but the reader is always taken step by step and even those without mathematical knowledge will still be able to follow the argument.

Each book has been written by an expert in his specific field, and should be regarded as a 'step' from the elementary to the technical field. Once this series of books has been read and digested, the student should be ready to proceed to more technical volumes. In addition each volume is complete in itself although, of course, the *Survey* will only be complete within the series as a whole.

The series is, then, designed for the benefit of the serious amateur and for the student. It is hoped that University students who are considering taking science degrees will find the books particularly useful.

Throughout the series the design of the volumes has been to give an up-to-date picture, indicating both present advances and also present limitations to our knowledge.

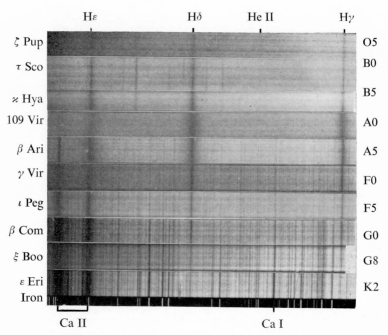

PLATE I. SPECTRA OF MAIN SEQUENCE STARS (O5 TO K2)

The bright lines of iron in the comparison spectrum at the bottom can be matched with dark lines in the coolest stars.

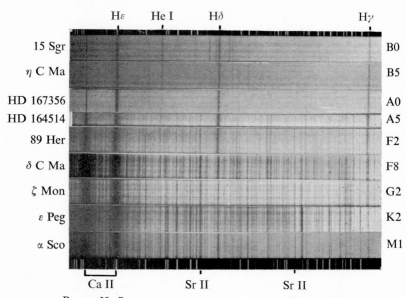

PLATE II. SPECTRA OF SUPERGIANT STARS (B0 TO M1)

Note the sharpness of the hydrogen lines compared with Plate I. (*Radcliffe Observatory photographs* × 10.)

ASTRONOMICAL
SPECTROSCOPY

by A. D. Thackeray

A SURVEY OF ASTRONOMY edited by Colin A. Ronan

The Macmillan Company · New York · 1961

CONTENTS

ILLUSTRATIONS

PLATES

(*on Frontispiece*)

PREFACE

Applications of the spectroscope to astronomy have been so innumerable that it is only possible to describe them very sketchily in a book of this nature. Accounts of some important researches have had to be reduced to a brief paragraph. Those that have been described in greater detail have been selected as examples demonstrating the power of the spectroscope in attacking otherwise insoluble problems. It is hoped that readers to whom the subject is new will be stimulated to seek further details in more advanced text-books on astrophysics. Any success which the book may enjoy in that direction will be traceable to the inspiration of my own tutors in astronomical spectroscopy.

I wish to thank Michael W. Feast for reading the manuscript and offering some helpful comments, also Mrs Charlotte Moore-Sitterly for assistance on several points.

A. D. T.

Radcliffe Observatory
Pretoria

Astronomical Spectroscopy

Chapter 1

THE BEGINNINGS

From prehistoric times Man's wonder has been excited by the sight of a rainbow. Raindrops, illuminated by parallel sunlight, form the simplest of spectroscopes. Traditionally, the magic number of seven was assigned to the colours of the rainbow, but the number of different shades of pure colours that can be separately recognized by the human eye in favourable conditions is very much greater. However, the human eye is a very poor judge of absolute colour, and for this purpose we require an instrument like a spectroscope, which bends each colour in a certain characteristic direction in controlled conditions. We can measure the direction for each colour objectively. Spectroscopy is the study of colour as an exact science.

It was probably sheer curiosity that led to Descartes' correct explanation of the rainbow (1637). But Newton's classical experiments (1666) on the nature of colour had a practical motive. He wished to make better telescopes, freed from the nuisance of coloured images produced by his simple lenses. He first gave the name *spectrum* to the continuous band of colours (R [red], G [green], V [violet]) into which white light (fig. 1*a*), emerging from a hole in a darkened room (on left of figure), was spread by a prism.

A second prism, placed immediately behind the first, simply gave a longer spectrum (fig. 1*b*) without the appearance of any new colours, and without any definite boundaries between the hues recognized by the eye. Finally, the composite

15

nature of white light was convincingly proved by reversing the second prism (fig. 1c); the screen then showed a white patch again.

For nearly two centuries after Newton's experiments the

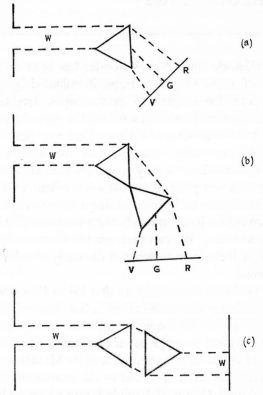

FIG. 1. Newton's experiments on white light.

spectroscope remained an almost unused toy. Newton must have come very close to detecting dark spaces in his spectrum of sunlight, and it is interesting to speculate what he would have thought of them if they had come to his notice. It was Wollaston (1802) who first discovered such gaps or *lines* by using a prism of better quality than Newton's and a narrow slit rather than a round hole – both factors involving a clearer resolution of different colours. In the laboratory Melvil (1752) discovered the yellow D lines emitted by sodium vapour. Wollaston also studied flame spectra but did not attempt any correlation with the dark lines in the spectrum of sunlight.

Shortly after Wollaston, Fraunhofer used a theodolite telescope to examine the spectrum of the Sun and was thus the first to look through a spectroscope in the true sense of the word. He was rewarded with the view of a bewildering number of lines, strong and weak, which he proceeded to map with care. The strongest were named by Fraunhofer A, B . . . to K in order from red to violet, and are still so called. (See Appendix I.)

The stage was now set for the new science of spectroscopy, but curiously there was a lag of some forty years before the real significance of the Fraunhofer lines was discovered. Several investigators examined the spectra of bright stars and noticed dark lines coinciding as far as they could tell with some of the solar Fraunhofer lines. It seems to have occurred to several minds independently that to each substance belonged a characteristic pattern of spectrum lines, but convincing proof was lacking. The extraordinary ease with which the two sodium lines, the Fraunhofer 'D' lines, can be excited, coupled with the fact that sodium was commonly present in laboratory substances as an unknown impurity, combined to bar the door to further progress until 1859. In that year Kirchhoff and Bunsen announced the results of their well-known experiments.

It was shown that the solar D lines coincided exactly in position with that of the bright lines emitted in the laboratory by a sodium flame, and further that if the Sun's rays were intercepted by the same sodium flame, the solar D lines appeared darker and wider; in other words, the sodium vapour

B

which appeared bright against a dark background (in the laboratory) could absorb exactly the same radiation which it emitted when placed in front of a hotter source (the Sun). Kirchhoff's law therefore stated that the ratio of the power of emission and the power of absorption at any given wavelength[1] is the same for all bodies at any given temperature. Thus if a body gives out a continuous spectrum (radiating all colours) it must be opaque (absorbing all colours). Again if a gas has a spectrum of bright lines it can only absorb at those wavelengths. The Fraunhofer spectrum was explained as due to the absorption of light from the hot, opaque, *photosphere* by the cooler gases above. Each dark line was to be attributed to absorption by some particular substance (in atomic or molecular form). Precise mapping of the bright lines given out by the various elements in laboratory spectra could lead to their being matched by the dark lines in the Sun's spectrum.

The impact of this discovery was startling and immediate. Here was the opportunity to study the physical composition of stars, a problem cited by the philosopher Auguste Comte only a few years before as one which could certainly never be solved. Here, too, was the opportunity to use the stars themselves as laboratories in conditions vastly different from those on Earth.

Simultaneously, it was realized by astronomers that the spectroscope also offered the opportunity to measure another

---

[1] If j_ν, k_ν are the coefficients of emission and absorption respectively at frequency ν, Kirchhoff's law states that in thermodynamic equilibrium j_ν/k_ν depends only on ν and the temperature T, not on the size, shape or composition of the substance. In mathematical form Kirchhoff's law now takes the form

$$\frac{j_\nu}{k_\nu} = 4\pi\frac{2h\nu^3}{c^2} \cdot \frac{1}{e^{h\nu/kT} - 1}$$

where h is Planck's constant
    k is Boltzmann's constant
    c is the velocity of light.

quantity hitherto regarded as inaccessible. The positions of stars had just begun to be measurable with sufficient accuracy for their trigonometrical parallaxes and proper motions to be detected; hence their actual speeds of motion across the line of sight could be determined. But the component of velocity towards or away from us (the *radial velocity*) appeared to be unobservable. However, Doppler showed that the velocity of approach changed the apparent pitch of sound, and that similar effects should occur in light on the apparent frequency or wavelength. Fizeau pointed out the usefulness of the Fraunhofer lines as standard 'markers' to be compared with the same 'markers' in the laboratory. The feasibility of measuring a star's radial velocity was now clear, and it only remained to develop instrumental techniques to realize this ambition.

Since each atom has its own characteristic pattern of lines, it was clear that each spectrum contained a clue as to the nature of the atom itself. It took many decades to unravel the clues, but it was to a large extent along the path of spectroscopy that the Bohr model of the atom and modern quantum mechanics were developed. The growth of atomic physics has been closely linked with the growth of astrophysics through the active use of the spectroscope. The astrophysicist is simultaneously concerned with the behaviour of atoms and of stars.

In what follows we shall be concerned with what the spectroscope has taught us about the stars in the past hundred years. Not only do we now know roughly what the stars are made of and how they are moving. We are able to measure distances of many stars too far away for trigonometrical methods. We can detect double stars which appear as one when viewed with the most powerful telescopes. We can weigh many stars. We can study matter spread between the stars so thinly that there is only about one atom per cubic centimetre. We can study radiations that have never been produced in the laboratory, but which can be attributed with certainty to familiar terrestrial atoms. The Sun is now known to be circling with its neighbours around a distant centre of the Milky Way; the Milky Way itself, a vast assemblage of stars, dust and gas, is being gradually mapped as a spiral nebula. Magnetic fields have been found in the Sun and in certain peculiar stars. We can investigate dynamic details on the Sun's surface and form vague pictures of similar phenomena on a grander scale near other stars. The cosmological problem of the century – 'the expanding universe' – rests on determining whether certain features in the spectra of these stars are due to their motions or possibly to some new principle of nature.

The stars are not eternal but are slowly changing from aeon to aeon, some much faster than others. There have been many theories to explain how stars are born, grow to maturity and die. In recent years the whole question of stellar evolution has begun to become clearer as a result of the pooling of knowledge gained by astrophysicists and laboratory physicists.

Much of this knowledge rests on the spectroscopist's measures of faint traces in black and white on photographic emulsions. This pursuit of 'exact colours' is far removed from the aesthetic pleasures of contemplating the beauties of nature. But the intellectual pursuit of new knowledge about stars and atoms can be just as inspiring as the first view of a rainbow.

Chapter 2

ASTRONOMICAL SPECTROSCOPES

Astronomers are concerned with such faint sources of light that economy of light has to be a prime consideration in the design of their instruments, and especially of their spectroscopes. Further, astronomical bodies show such an enormous range in apparent brightness that different types of spectroscope are required according to the particular objects which are to be studied. The faintest stars whose spectra have been observed are about a hundred million times fainter than Sirius (a range of 20 stellar magnitudes), while the magnitude of Sirius is itself 25 magnitudes fainter than that of the Sun.

The essential component of any spectroscope is the dispersing medium which sorts the incident light into different directions according to the wavelength. The rest of the optical parts have to be designed to bring the resulting spectrum into as sharp a focus as possible and to give it an appropriate length; in order to see fine detail we would like to use a large scale, but the fainter the light-source the shorter is the spectrum that we have to be satisfied with. There are two dispersing media commonly used, the prism (usually of glass which must be highly homogeneous) and the diffraction grating.

Prisms. Three types of prisms are illustrated in fig. 2. In 2(*a*), the commonest type, the principal section (perpendicular to the edges) is in the form of an equilateral triangle *ABC*. Light incident on the face *AB* is refracted through different angles according to the wavelength. This angular dispersion

21

per unit wavelength varies according to the substance of the prism. On emerging from the face *BC* the light is further refracted and dispersed. In the final spectrum the red rays (R) suffer least refraction, the green (G) more and the violet rays (V) the most.

In 2(*b*) we have a 30° prism, the equivalent of a 60° prism cut in two. Light passing through such a prism would be dispersed to only half the extent that it is in 2(*a*). But if we provide the face *BC* with some reflecting material, say silver or aluminium, then the rays emerge again from the face *AB* dispersed by the same amount as in 2(*a*). This prism therefore disperses and reflects, the dispersed beam being exactly

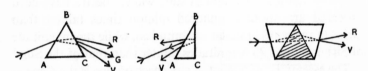

(a)   (b)   (c)

FIG. 2. Three forms of dispersion in a prism. R = red, G = green, V = violet.

opposite to the incident beam, without displacement. This can be of advantage in certain cases.

In 2(*c*) we have a direct-vision prism formed of three (or more) prisms cemented together, the inner one being made of a different substance from the outer two. Here the light is dispersed but not deviated, at least for the central ray. The dispersion of such a prism is too small for most astronomical purposes, but it is useful as a pocket instrument for direct examination of a source of light.

In passing we may note various devices whereby a prism can be used without dispersing the incident light. Three such devices are shown in fig. 3. In 3(*a*) we have a right-angled prism as frequently used for deviating light through 90° without dispersion. Light enters and leaves the prism normal to the surface with total internal reflection at AC. There is thus no dispersion. The prism serves precisely the same purpose as a plane mirror but without the disadvantage of gradual tarnishing.

3(b) shows a similar device whereby a right-angled prism can be used to reflect a beam through 180° and simultaneously displace it.

3(c) shows the passage of parallel light through a prism along the direction of the hypotenuse. In this case there is dispersion within the prism, but all the colours emerge in a parallel beam; there is only slight colouring at the edges of

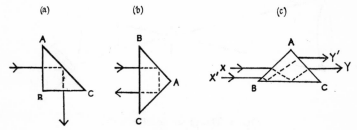

FIG. 3. Three uses of a right-angled prism without dispersion.

the beam. If such a prism is rotated about the line XY through an angle θ it will be found that the emerging beam is rotated through 2θ. (It can easily be verified that if the prism is rotated through 180° with the apex A of the prism at the bottom, the emergent beam Y' will still appear above Y as in the figure; Y' will have been rotated through 360°.) Such an image rotator is required for some astronomical observations.

The prism spectroscope. Fig. 4 illustrates a standard spectroscope comprising one 60° prism.

An objective O (drawn as a lens although it might equally well be a concave mirror) forms an image on a slit S. The slit is placed at the focus of a collimating lens C, the purpose of which is to pass a beam of parallel light to the prism. The prism bends the various colours through different angles depending on its own orientation in the beam. It is customarily oriented in that position which bends *least* the colour which it is desired to study – that is the position of *minimum deviation* for the wavelength concerned. The spectrum emerging from the prism may then be examined visually with a telescope focused for infinity, or more customarily a camera lens C' focuses the spectrum on a photographic plate.

In order to give the best results the spectroscope must be adjusted so that:

(1) The slit jaws are parallel to the edges of the prism.

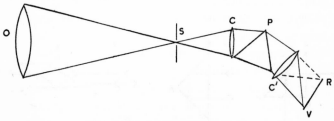

FIG. 4. The prism spectroscope.

(2) The collimator lens is adjusted to feed parallel light to the prism.

(3) The direction of the parallel beam is perpendicular to the edges of the prism.

(4) The prism is set at minimum deviation for the wavelength required.

Conditions (1) and (3) are purely geometrical, but conditions (2) and (4) depend upon the wavelength of the light being studied. For instance, no lens is perfectly achromatic in bringing all colours to precisely the same focus. Thus, if we adjust the distance slit-collimator to feed a parallel beam of green rays to the prism, the violet and red rays will not be strictly parallel. This difficulty need not be a serious one.

The camera lens C' is designed to have two, three or four components but need not be perfectly achromatic. Small differences in focal length for different wavelengths can easily be taken up by merely tilting the photographic plate (as in fig. 4 where the photographic plate RV is not square on to the camera lens C'). It is however of some importance that the focal surface should be flat, so that with a suitable tilt a wide range of wavelengths will be sharply focused on the plate. Stellar spectra often require long exposures and it is obviously advantageous to record as long a spectrum in focus at one time as possible. If necessary, film can be used in a curved focal surface, but film is more liable to troublesome distortions than an emulsion on a glass plate.

Through the ingenious balancing of optical aberrations it has been possible to design spectrographs utilizing prisms and lenses in which one can record satisfactorily sharp spectra over a range of 3000 angstroms (usually written A) from the red to the ultra-violet in one exposure on plates.

One great disadvantage in the use of glass in prisms and lenses is that most glasses absorb ultra-violet wavelengths heavily so that it is uneconomical to observe spectra beyond a wavelength of 3900 A in this way. If it is desired to investigate the region from 3900 to 3000 A (at which latter limit absorption by atmospheric ozone prevents further astronomical observations) the use of quartz or special ultra-violet glass is essential for prisms and lenses. Such materials are, however, expensive and difficult to obtain in the size and homogeneity required. Observations in the ultra-violet can be made much more satisfactorily with modern diffraction gratings.

The diffraction grating. The simplest type of grating consists of a set of fine wires spaced at very close regular intervals (e.g. by winding round two screws of small pitch). Light transmitted through such a grating either passes straight through or appears as a series of spectra. The different spectra are referred to as different '*orders*' (see fig. 5). Through the destructive interference of the waves of the diffracted beam, light of wavelength λ will only appear in directions of angle θ given by the fundamental equation[1]

$$n\lambda = b \sin \theta$$

where n is an integer (representing the first, second, third

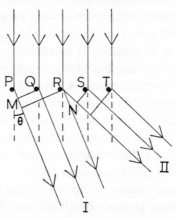

Fig. 5. The diffraction grating. Parallel light incident on a set of equally spaced wires P, Q, R, S, T either passes straight through or is diffracted into coloured 'orders' I, II, etc. The condition for reinforcement of light-waves is that the differences in light-path of adjacent rays (e.g. PM or RN) should be $n\lambda$ (n = whole number, λ = wavelength). In the examples shown, $PM = \lambda$, $RN = 2\lambda$, corresponding to the first and second orders.

'order', etc.) and b is the distance between adjacent wires. It can easily be seen from this equation that the spread or dispersion of the diffracted beam (that is the change of θ with λ or mathematically $d\theta/d\lambda$) is proportional to n and in-

---

[1] This is for the simple case when, as in fig. 5, the incident light is normal to the grating. In the more general case when the angle of incidence is α and the angle of the diffracted ray is β, we have

$$n\lambda = b(\sin \alpha + \sin \beta)$$

dependent of λ. The dispersion in the second order is twice that of the first, but is constant along the spectrum in any order. (By contrast, in a prism spectroscope the dispersion increases towards shorter wavelengths.)

The different orders overlap so that, for instance, infrared light at 8000 A in the first order coincides with violet light of 4000 A in the second order. This overlapping is not troublesome unless one uses the third or higher orders.

In the last century and until about 1930 much use was made of gratings consisting of fine grooves ruled on speculum metal. These were of the common reflecting type instead of the transmitting type illustrated in fig. 5. Rowland, and later Michelson, constructed excellent gratings, either on plane or concave surfaces, which were used with great effect on the solar spectrum. The overlapping orders were of great service in the days before satisfactory standard wavelengths were set up, because they automatically set the scale over a wide range in a manner that was impossible with a prism. But astronomically, gratings were not often used except for the solar spectrum because of their wastefulness of light.

In the 1930's two technical developments took place which immediately promoted diffraction gratings to the position of a serious competitor with prisms in astronomical spectrographs. The first was the process of depositing aluminium on glass surfaces under vacuum. The second was the production of specially ruled or 'blazed' gratings which cast a large percentage of the incident light into one prescribed order, and thus gave as bright a spectrum as possible and comparable with that of a prism.

The size of the speculum gratings produced by Rowland had been limited by the fact that after ruling 6 inches of surface at 15,000 grooves per inch, the diamond became worn so that the shape of the grooves gradually became less sharp. It was found that if rulings were made in aluminium deposited on glass, much greater areas could be ruled uniformly without appreciable wear on the diamond. The resolving power of a spectrograph depends on the total number of usable grooves in a grating or on the effective aperture of a prism. It became obvious that the production of a high-quality aluminized grating (at 15,000 lines per inch or even more) with aperture 6 or 8 inches was a much easier task than that of a homogeneous prism of equal resolving power. However, the inefficiency of a grating in casting light into many orders still told in favour of prisms.

But again the technique of ruling on aluminium became sufficiently controlled that the grooves could be made steeper on one side than the other (see fig. 6). With this shape *accurately maintained* from beginning to end of the process of ruling, a great proportion of the light could be concentrated in one order. This 'blazing' process could be adapted

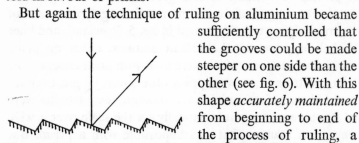

FIG. 6. A blazed grating sends a spectrum strongly in one direction depending on the shape of the grooves.

so that one could choose the most efficient order in which to work. The fundamental equation still holds, of course, so that for instance a grating blazed for second order 4500 A, will be blazed for first order 9000 A or third order 3000 A. At intermediate wavelengths the efficiency falls, but if necessary these regions could be studied with another grating with a suitable blaze. In the best modern gratings about 70 per cent of the incident light can be blazed into a specified direction.

Side by side with this increased efficiency of gratings, the transmission of glass lenses and prisms has been increased by the technique of 'blooming' glass surfaces. At such surfaces when there is a sudden change in refractive index due to the lens being in contact with air, an unwanted reflection of some 5 per cent of the incident light occurs. In an optical beam where there may be as many as ten of these air–glass surfaces the accumulated loss of light is substantial. However, by coating the surfaces with some substance such as lithium fluoride the change in refractive index is rendered gradual rather than abrupt. Loss by reflection then becomes negligibly small.

In concluding this comparison of the merits of prisms and gratings it must be pointed out, first, that gratings tend to produce more scattered light within the spectroscope than prisms; and secondly they produce spurious lines known as 'ghosts' which do not occur with prisms at all. These 'ghosts' are due to small periodic errors in the ruling machine and consist of equally spaced lines on both sides of strong lines. The total intensity of the ghosts may amount to a few per cent of the parent line. In a spectrum of emission lines care has to be taken to recognize the ghosts, while in refined spectro-photometry of absorption lines allowance must be made for the influence of overlapping ghosts from the continuous spectrum.

Cameras for spectroscopes. Astronomical spectroscopes are usually provided with two or more cameras which can be readily interchanged. In this way spectra of stars covering a large range of brightness can be photographed with toler-able exposure times. Bright stars are observed with long cameras giving long spectra, while for faint stars we have to be content with short spectra showing less detail. When inter-changing cameras it is obvious that the only adjustment required refers to the camera itself and to no other part of the spectroscope.

To meet the astronomer's need for speed it is difficult to design faster lenses than $f/2$ with adequate field of good definition. A remarkable achievement in the spectroscopic

observation of distant extragalactic nebulae was the successful use of a f/0·6 lens, using oil immersion, based on principles
developed for microscopic objectives. However, the development of the Schmidt camera (fig. 7) eased considerably the
design of such short-focus cameras.

The classical Schmidt camera uses a spherical mirror M as
objective, the spherical aberration being corrected by a thin
plate P placed at the mirror's centre of curvature. The focal
surface F (which is curved) lies midway between plate and
mirror. The system is free from chromatic aberration except
for a small amount introduced by the correcting plate itself.
The great advantage of the Schmidt camera over a parabolic

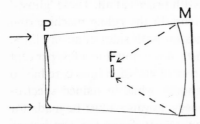

mirror lies in the extension
of the angular field of
good definition. This al-
lows astronomers to re-
alize their ambition to
record long stretches of
spectrum in one photo-
graph. During the last two
decades systems employ-

FIG. 7. Classical Schmidt Camera.

ing mirrors and gratings have to a large extent become
preferred over lens–prism combinations. The elimination of
any glass in the light-beam (apart from the thin correcting plate of the Schmidt camera) has many advantages,
especially for observations in the ultra-violet.

Resolving power of spectroscopes. If a spectroscope will just
resolve two lines of wavelength λ separated by an interval $d\lambda$,
we define the resolving power as $\lambda/d\lambda$, a pure number. It is
obvious that progress in astronomical knowledge will result
from the use of spectroscopes with the highest possible
resolving power. In practice, values of over a million have
been realized for the spectrum of the Sun, while values of only
a few hundred can be usefully applied to faint stars.

If $d\theta/d\lambda$ is the angular dispersion[1] of a prism or grating, the scale of the spectrum at the focus of the camera, that is the linear dispersion, is $f_2 . d\theta/d\lambda$, where f_2 is the focal length of the camera. We can increase the linear dispersion indefinitely by increasing f_2, but the resolving power can only be increased by introducing a more powerful dispersing medium. The limit is set by the fact that light is diffracted at a narrow slit. The diffraction pattern has an angular size depending on the aperture of the collimator.

Theoretically, the resolving power is independent of the focal length of the camera. In practice, when photographing spectra with short cameras the limit of resolution is set by the graininess of the photographic emulsion. Fineness of grain is always associated with low sensitivity. The fast emulsions commonly used in astronomy have resolution of about 0·02 mm. This has to be borne in mind when deciding on the width of slit to be used. To achieve theoretical resolving power the slit must be closed until the collimator lens just accepts the central maximum of the diffraction pattern formed by the slit and no more. But if the image of the slit formed by the camera is less than 0·02 mm we can afford to widen the slit.

Seeing. Why, it may be asked, should we want to widen the slit when observing a star which has a point-image? The answer is that owing to disturbances in the Earth's atmosphere, which vary from night to night or even in fractions of a second, our conditions for 'seeing' the star images vary. Large telescopes form images of stars with perceptible diameters ranging from less than a second of arc in the calmest conditions to over ten seconds of arc in the most disturbed. A small telescope may show a point-like image surrounded by diffraction rings, but the image will be dancing about due to the atmospheric waves which are larger than the aperture of

[1] See Glossary.

the telescope. If the aperture of the telescope is larger than the waves, the motion of the image becomes less marked and one sees a blurred image (composed of a whole family of dancing points). A large telescope gives a small diffraction pattern (inversely proportional to the aperture) so that one should be able to resolve close double stars; but the diffraction pattern is frequently lost in the atmospheric disturbances. A visual double star observer can snatch the few moments of excellent 'seeing' to make his measures; but in photographing spectra we have to deal with average conditions over long periods of time.

In conditions of bad 'seeing' the slit may transmit less than 10 per cent of the light in a stellar image. The quality of seeing controls the exposures required for slit spectroscopy more than any other factor. It is clear that widening the slit, if it can be done without loss of resolving power, will be of advantage. Due to 'seeing' the image of a star fed by a large modern reflector to a spectrograph may often be as large as 1 mm or considerably larger. Stellar spectra have to have a certain width in order to see the lines and this is achieved by trailing the star up and down the slit during the exposure. This procedure may become superfluous in bad 'seeing' with a large telescope. In these conditions one reaches the surprising conclusion that *the speed of a spectroscope will not be increased by using a still larger telescope*. Suppose a spectroscope working with a telescope of aperture D and focal length f be transferred to a telescope of aperture $2D$ and focal length $2f$ (the focal ratio must be preserved in order to fill the collimator). The linear diameter of a stellar image, assumed to be controlled by the same average 'seeing' in the two cases, will be twice as great for the larger telescope, but its *surface brightness* will be the same. The slit-width of the spectrograph must be held constant to preserve resolving power, and therefore there will be a loss of light at the slit just balancing the gain of light due to the larger telescope. The larger the telescope, the more one is dependent on good 'seeing' for its efficient use in spectroscopy.

The general rules covering the design of efficient slit spectroscopes for large telescopes may be summarized as follows:

(1) the collimator, working at the same focal ratio as the telescope, should be large;

(2) the dispersing medium, utilizing the whole of the collimator, should have large angular resolution;

(3) the ratio of focal lengths f_1/f_2 (collimator/camera) should be large, permitting the use of a widened slit.

Mounting of spectroscopes. Reflecting telescopes are commonly used in one of four ways illustrated in the figure; either at the prime focus, the Newtonian, Cassegrain or coudé foci.

Fig. 8(*a*) shows that the use of the prime focus *P* necessitates mounting the spectroscope within the incident beam, at the top of the tube; alternatively the Newtonian focus *N* is fed by a 45° flat mirror. In 8(*b*), the Cassegrain focus is fed, through a hole in the centre of the primary mirror, by a hyperboloid mirror *C* which increases the focal length. In 8(*c*) another hyperboloid mirror *C'*, lengthening the focus still more, feeds the beam through two flat mirrors down the polar axis of the telescope to a focus at *C'F*, known as the coudé focus. The great advantage of the coudé focus is that it remains fixed in space as the telescope swings in following a star across the sky. Spectroscopes at primary, Newtonian or Cassegrain foci, have to be carried on the moving telescope, and the whole construction is liable to *flexure* as the spectroscope hangs at varying angles to the direction of gravity. At the coudé focus we can mount massive parts, as in a laboratory, without having to consider such problems. A further advantage of the coudé focus is that the primary mirror is

c

used at a large focal ratio, and it is relatively easy to ensure a large ratio f_1/f_2 within the spectroscope, which, as we have seen, is one of the criteria of efficiency. On the other hand, the system of mirrors employed for work at the coudé focus gives rise to a rotation of the field as the telescope moves. This is of no consequence for most stellar work. But if one

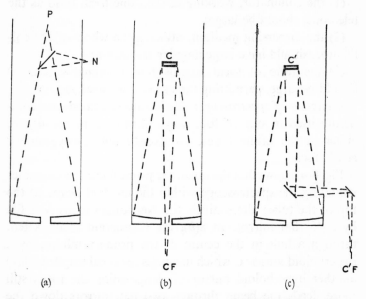

FIG. 8. Various forms of reflecting telescope: (*a*) shows the prime focus *P* and the Newtonian focus *N*: (*b*) and (*c*) show particular forms of Cassegrain (*CF*) and coudé (*C'F*) foci respectively.

wishes to keep an extended object like a nebula orientated in a constant direction along the slit, this can be done with the help of an image rotator.

Nebular spectroscopes. A special type of spectroscope, developed by Struve at the Yerkes and Macdonald Observatories, records with maximum efficiency the spectra of faint nebulae diffused through the Milky Way. All that is required is a coarse slit, several inches wide, a prism and a very short camera. The slit is placed so far from the rest of the spectroscope (150 feet at the Macdonald Observatory) that no collimator is required; the light falling on the prism is nearly parallel. The long instrument does not have to be moved to follow the diurnal motion of the sky because it can be fed by a moving mirror system or coelostat; with the spectroscope mounted at an angle parallel to the Earth's axis, the coelostat requires only one mirror which moves in such a way that the image of any star remains stationary. A screen between slit and prism is necessary to suppress stray skylight.

The instrument records spectra of the sky covering areas about $2° \times \frac{1}{4}°$. It is ideal for the study of faint nebulae greater than $\frac{1}{4}°$ in diameter. It is remarkable that important observations can be made with such a simple instrument which does not require a telescope at all. Large telescopes become useful for nebular spectroscopy when it is desired to study fine details covering much less than $\frac{1}{4}°$.

Slitless spectroscopes. Very useful spectra can also be obtained without using a slit at all. If a field of stars is photographed with a prism (usually of angle about 5° to 12°) in front of the objective, each stellar image is spread into a little streak in which the strongest spectrum lines can be detected.

The 'objective prism' has the enormous advantage over the slit spectroscope in that one single exposure can record hundreds of stellar spectra while the slit spectroscope can only concentrate on one star at a time. Moreover, elimination of the slit means that quite faint stars can be studied with fairly small telescopes of about 10 inches aperture. Objective prism spectra are invaluable for roughly classifying large numbers of stars.

To offset these advantages the quality of slitless spectra is naturally inferior to those obtained with slit. Any imperfections in guiding of the telescope or in astronomical 'seeing' will blur such spectra; with a slit these errors only mean that the exposure time should be lengthened. Further, no terrestrial standard spectrum can be put beside the stellar spectra, as is invariably done when using a slit. This has ruled out, until recent years, the possibility of measuring radial velocities of stars with objective prisms.

A slitless spectroscope (complete with collimator), attached to a telescope, has special uses on objects like planetary nebulae, with spectra consisting of bright lines. At the position of each line one has a monochromatic image of the nebula which tells us about the distribution of the gas responsible for the bright line (p. 134).

In the case of the Sun, it was discovered at an early date (1868) that with a spectroscope in which the slit was greatly widened one could see, just outside the edge of the Sun, images of the clouds of gas known as 'prominences' in hydrogen light. Wide circular slits fitted to the image of the Sun showed at a glance the positions and shapes of the brightest prominences.

The spectroheliograph. The observation of solar prominences without an eclipse led to the development of this specialized solar instrument in which monochromatic images of the Sun in hydrogen or calcium light could be photographed. A narrow slit is used with a high-dispersion spectroscope, and a second slit is placed at the focus exactly coincident with the position of the strongest accessible hydrogen or calcium line. A photographic plate immediately behind the second slit gives a monochromatic image of only this narrow slit-section of the Sun's disk. By moving the telescope objective and photographic plate at the same uniform speed a monochromatic image of the whole disk is built up. The process is similar to building up a picture on a television screen with a set tuned to a particular wavelength.

The spectrohelioscope is a similar device for viewing a

considerable portion of the Sun's disk in hydrogen light. In some forms it used rapidly oscillating slits, but the standard form has rotating rectangular prisms beside fixed slits which serve the same purpose. In this form it has been widely used for international monitoring of the Sun's surface in a watch for short-lived solar disturbances.

Ciné-photography of prominences and other solar phenomena has been achieved with the *spectroheliokinematograph*.

Narrow-band filters. Filters which use interference or polarizing properties of light have been developed which pass only narrow stretches of the spectrum of the order of 10 A wide. These provide very simple alternatives to an instrument like the spectroheliograph. Besides solar work they have also been used profitably on bright-line objects like nebulae.

Light detectors. By far the commonest method of recording astronomical spectra is still photographic. Despite the faintness of astronomical sources, photographic emulsions will build up dense images simply by increasing exposure times. Fast emulsions used for high-speed photography in daylight are inefficient for most astronomical work, but remarkably fast emulsions have been developed specially suited for work at low levels of intensity. Astronomers also owe much to the photographic technician in producing fast emulsions sensitive to the red and infra-red.

Photo-electric cells have been used to study stellar spectra and it is to be expected that in time this technique will replace the photographic approach in some fields. The photo-electric technique is particularly valuable when one wishes to measure the brightness in small stretches of the spectrum with high accuracy. The photographic method is still to be preferred when one wishes to 'scan' a wide range of wavelengths simultaneously.

A combined photographic and photo-electric technique for simultaneous scanning of whole spectra has been developed with remarkable success by Lallemand. The ejected photo-electrons from a cathode of a photo-electric cell are focused on to a photographic emulsion. The emulsion has to be mounted in the same vacuum with the photo-cell. The speed achieved is about 100 times that of the photographic plate. Development of such techniques is likely to revolutionize all branches of astronomy.

Chapter 3

SERIES IN ATOMIC SPECTRA
AND ENERGY LEVELS

The full significance of the spectra of astronomical bodies cannot be grasped without an understanding of the basic principles of how atoms and molecules behave in order to produce their characteristic patterns of lines and bands. Historically, the first steps toward this understanding were made empirically, and for the purpose of this book an empirical approach will suffice.

Liveing and Dewar (1879) discovered that many lines due to the element sodium could be grouped into three overlapping series of lines, and that each component of the series consisted of a close pair of lines – the famous D lines (see Chap. 1, p. 17) being typical. Hartley (1883) showed that the separation of these pairs remained constant along these series when measured in frequencies v or wave-numbers $\tilde{v}$ instead of wavelengths λ.[1] Hartley found that this law applied also to three-line groups (triplets) shown by magnesium. It gave the clue that frequencies are more important than wavelengths.

Soon afterwards, Balmer (1885) succeeded in fitting the wavelengths of the strongest lines of hydrogen to a numerical formula; the positions of these lines followed a regular pattern, and so could be predicted. Actually, only four lines of

[1] The frequency, $v = c/\lambda$, where c is the velocity of light, is the number of vibrations per second; the wave-number $\tilde{v} = 1/\lambda$ is the number of waves per cm. at a particular wavelength.

the *Balmer series*[1] are readily visible to the eye, and it must be remembered that in laboratories of those days the hydrogen spectrum was not too easily excited. Huggins' observations of some stars provided the only data concerning the ultra-violet end of the Balmer series. Modern work has naturally extended it much further.

Rydberg extended Balmer's work, and showed that by using wave-numbers, Balmer's formula became only a particular case of a general formula[2] which was obeyed by many other atoms. Moreover, this formula contained a constant (Rydberg's constant) which remained *the same for all atoms investigated.*

As laboratory techniques were improved, new series of lines were found in the hydrogen spectrum, in the far ultra-violet, by Lyman; and in the infra-red by Paschen, Brackett and Pfund.[3]

The stage was now set for Bohr to explain the spectrum of hydrogen by means of his atomic model (1913). The hydrogen atom, with its positively charged nucleus, 1837 times as massive as its single negatively charged electron, may be regarded

---

[1] Balmer's series is given by $\lambda = x\dfrac{n^2}{n^2 - 4}$, where n is an integer greater than 2.

[2] Balmer's series takes the form for wave-numbers $\tilde{\nu} = R\left(\dfrac{1}{2^2} - \dfrac{1}{n^2}\right)$.

Rydberg's general formula for series of lines in many atoms was of the form

$$\tilde{\nu} = \tilde{\nu}_\infty - \frac{R}{(n + \mu)^2}$$

where n is a series of integers, ν_∞ is the series limit as n becomes infinite, and R and μ are constants. This reduces to Balmer's formula when $\mu = 0$.

[3] These series were expected, from the generalization of Balmer's formula in the form $\tilde{\nu} = R\left(\dfrac{1}{m^2} - \dfrac{1}{n^2}\right)$. The Lyman series is given by $m = 1$; the Paschen, Brackett and Pfund series by $m = 3$, 4 and 5 respectively.

as a miniature Solar System. In the atom, however, Bohr visualized electrostatic forces dominant in place of the gravitational forces of the Solar System. And whereas an infinite number of orbits are possible within the Solar System, the *quantum conditions* postulated by Bohr restrict the orbits of the electron to those for which the total energy E (that is the sum of all forms of energy – kinetic and potential – which a moving electron can have) takes only certain values.[1]

It is not easy to put this into plain language, and we must beware of the tempting picture of an atom as made up of solid lumps of material. However, there is no harm in drawing an analogy. Suppose that for some reason the Earth's motion were disturbed by an outside force, so that its orbit were changed. The present mean distance from the Sun is almost exactly 93,000,000 miles. We can picture a situation in which the mean distance could be increased to – say – 95,000,000 or 100,000,000 miles; in fact, to any value, either greater or less than the present one. This is not the case with an atom. The planetary electron is not free to adopt any orbit; if it changes its orbit at all, it must do so with a definite 'jump' to another definite orbit – it cannot jump 'in between'.

One of Bohr's postulates was that the hydrogen atom can suddenly change from one orbit, or level, of energy E_n to another of energy E_m, and that in so doing it emits or absorbs a *quantum* of radiation.[2] If the atom ends in a state of lower energy after the change, a quantum of frequency v is emitted

[1] The restricted values of the energy are given by
$$E = \text{constant} - Rhc/n^2,$$
where R is Rydberg's constant, h is Planck's constant, c the velocity of light, and n is any integer.

[2] The frequency v of the radiation in such a transition is given by
$$E_n - E_m = hv$$
This surprising proportionality of *energy* to *frequency* of radiation had already been postulated by Planck (1900) to explain features in continuous spectra.

giving a bright line in the spectrum; if the atom ends in a higher state of energy, a quantum is absorbed.

A single line in the spectrum is thus linked with the transition of an electron between two energy levels. The observ-

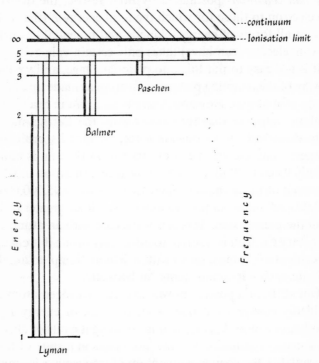

FIG. 9. Grotrian diagram of Hydrogen. The heights of the vertical lines correspond to the frequencies of the spectrum lines in each series.

ation of bright and dark lines at the same wavelength, or frequency, is thus satisfactorily explained.

The situation for hydrogen may be conveniently represented in the form of fig. 9. The height above the lowest horizontal line, numbered 1, corresponds to the relative energy in the various levels; and according to Bohr's postulate, this difference in energy between any two levels is proportional to the frequency of the corresponding line emitted or absorbed. We can now see why the series are so regular; each 'jump' has to be by a set amount. The series of transitions 1–2, 1–3, 1–4, etc., corresponds to the Lyman series; the transitions 2–3, 2–4, etc., to the Balmer series; and so on.

Ionization and Excitation. The heavy line at the top of fig. 9 corresponds to the energy of the hydrogen atom when its single electron has been completely removed (with zero energy for the free electron). When an atom has lost one of its electrons, it is said to be *ionized*. Hydrogen can be only singly ionized, since it has only one electron to lose; but more complex atoms may lose two or more electrons, become doubly ionized, triply ionized, etc.

Each series of lines converges to a definite limit, the 'ionization limit'. The atom can absorb still more energy in the process of ionization if the free electron is given extra kinetic energy; no quantum conditions restrict the amount of kinetic energy which can be taken up by the free electron, and therefore we have a continuous band of energy levels beyond the ionization limit. In hot stars, Huggins had observed (long before Bohr proposed this model) an absorption band beyond the limit of the Balmer series, and this was now recognized as being due to this process of ionization; theory and observation fitted perfectly. At the 1898 solar eclipse, Evershed discovered the same band in emission in the Sun's upper atmosphere; this was due to the reverse process of ionized hydrogen atoms capturing energetic free electrons.

From fig. 9, it may easily be seen that the difference in frequency between the Lyman and Balmer limits should be exactly equal to the frequency of the transition 1–2 (known as Lyman α); this is found to be the case. The analysis of atomic spectra is rich in such cross-checks, thereby giving great confidence in the correctness of the results.

The energy of each level is usually measured in units of electron volts. This is the number of volts required to raise an electron to an energy level above the ground-level or normal state of the atom, which is taken as zero. In the state 2 the hydrogen atom is excited to an energy of 10·13 volts, and this is called the *excitation potential* of the second level. In some classical experiments, Franck and Hertz (1914) bombarded various gases with electrons which had been accelerated with increasing voltage, and proved the existence of certain critical potentials. With sodium, for instance, as soon as the electrons had enough energy to excite the D lines (2·1 volts) they were stopped by collision, and the measured current fell. Such experiments gave a direct link between measures of energy (in volts) and spectroscopic frequencies.

The minimum energy for ionization of hydrogen from the lowest level is 13·5 volts, and this, therefore, is the ionization potential for hydrogen. Having lost its one electron, the remaining proton (i.e. the nucleus of the atom) is unable to yield a line spectrum until it recaptures an electron. For atoms possessing many electrons, however, new series of lines may be found according to whether one, two or more electrons are removed.

Sodium. The situation for sodium is rather more complicated than for hydrogen – which is understandable, since the sodium atom is a more complex structure. The situation is represented in fig. 10. Here, instead of a single series of levels, as for hydrogen, there is a set of series which have been called S, P, D, F, etc. (from the descriptions of the lines as sharp, principal, diffuse and fundamental). The principal series contains the strongest lines in the spectrum, and consists of the transitions 3S to nP in the diagram. The series 3P to nS gives rise to sharp lines, and 3P to nD to diffuse lines.

Since sodium has eleven electrons compared with the one of hydrogen, it may seem surprising at first that its spectrum is not still more complicated. But the general pattern of fig. 10 (often called a Grotrian diagram after the German physicist W. Grotrian who recognized their utility) is typical of all the alkali metals; lithium, sodium, potassium, rubidium, caesium. The chemical properties of these elements depend upon their having one valence electron – that is to say, one electron outside the furthest complete 'shell' from the nucleus. Each one of them has one more electron than an inert gas (helium, neon, etc.) in which the electrons form a stable closed shell.

The fact that the inert gases have no valence electrons

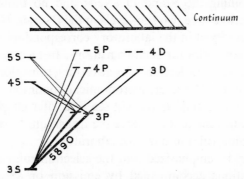

FIG. 10. Grotrian diagram of Na I. The heavily drawn lines (3*S* to 3*P*) correspond to the D lines.

prevents their entering into chemical combinations. Alkali metals, however, readily do so, and moreover the single valence electron is relatively easily detached. It is true to say that the optical spectrum of any atom depends upon the number of valence electrons, and it is instructive to compare the Grotrian diagrams of elements which occupy similar positions in the Periodic Table.

It will be noticed in fig. 9 that the P and D series consist of two closely adjacent levels, but that the S levels are drawn single. This state of affairs gives rise to doublets such as the D lines (3S–3P). It is due to a small amount of energy contributed by the spin of the electron itself. According to quantum theory, this energy must have a certain value, positive or negative according to the direction of the spin.

Selection rules. Although fig. 10 is more complicated than the figure diagram for hydrogen, it is far less complicated than it might be. In the hydrogen spectrum, lines corresponding to transitions between *all* the levels of fig. 9 can be observed. In fig. 10 no transitions are drawn connecting members of the same series of levels vertically; no transitions are drawn joining the S and D levels; and no transitions are drawn between the two sub-levels in the P series. No lines are usually observed in the laboratory corresponding to the predicted frequencies for such transitions. In fact, we find that there are definite selection rules governing transitions between atomic states. However, astronomical conditions are much more extreme, and, as we will see in a later chapter, astronomers can sometimes observe the transitions 'forbidden' by the selection rules in our own laboratories.

It must be emphasized that the selection rules apply only to transitions accompanied by emission or absorption of radiation. In collisions with other atoms or electrons, transitions between *any* two levels can occur. The overriding rule that has to be obeyed in a collision is the conservation of energy. Thus if an atom is excited in a collision to a higher level, thus gaining energy of excitation E, the total kinetic energy of the colliding particles must be diminished by the same quantity E.

Magnesium. The spectrum of this element includes series of single lines and series of triplets. In the Grotrian diagram for magnesium (fig. 11) we notice series of single S, P, D . . . levels and also different series of triplet S, P, D . . . levels (although the S 'triplets' are in fact single). Combinations between singlet and triplet levels are not in general observed;

but this selection rule is one which tends to be violated more and more frequently as one deals with increasingly complex atoms. In magnesium, a transition between the lowest ^{1}S state and the middle of the three lowest ^{3}P states gives rise to an astrophysically important line (4571 A).

It has been mentioned that the doublets of sodium are due to the spin-energy of the single valence electron. In general, the multiplicity of levels of an atom is directly related to the number of valence electrons. Magnesium, with two valence

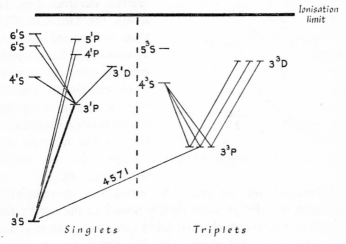

FIG. 11. Grotrian diagram of Mg I.

electrons, has singlets and triplets; aluminium, with three valence electrons, has doublets and quartets.

Just as fig. 10 is typical of alkali metals, so fig. 11 is typical of alkaline earths: beryllium, calcium, etc.

Ionized atoms. It has been remarked that if hydrogen is ionized, the remaining proton cannot by itself give rise to a line-spectrum. Helium is an inert gas. If however helium loses one of its two planetary electrons, the resulting ion or ionized atom resembles the hydrogen atom, except that the helium nucleus has four times the mass of the proton and twice as great a positive charge.

The spectrum of ionized helium was first observed by E. C. Pickering in the hottest stars. Alternate members of the so-called Pickering series coincide closely with the Balmer series for hydrogen.[1]

If we consider ionized magnesium or ionized calcium, both these ions resemble sodium in having one valence electron. Fig. 12 shows the Grotrian diagram for ionized calcium. The strongest lines, which can be seen to correspond exactly to the D lines of sodium in fig. 10, are the famous Fraunhofer lines H and K, easily the strongest in the visible solar spectrum.

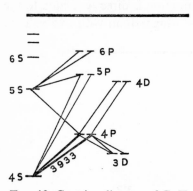

FIG. 12. Grotrian diagram of Ca II.

When an atom loses one or more electrons, the remaining electrons are always more tightly bound to the ion by the positively charged nucleus. It takes more energy to raise the electrons to excited levels. This has the important astro-

[1] Wave-numbers for the Pickering series can be closely represented by the Balmer formula for hydrogen if we allow n to take half-integral values. Alternatively, if we retain the condition of only integral values for n, we may write for ionized helium

$$\tilde{\nu} = 4R\left(\frac{1}{4^2} - \frac{1}{n^2}\right)$$

Bohr's model predicted such a series for ionized helium, because his calculated Rydberg constant included the square of the charge on the nucleus and should therefore be four times the value for hydrogen. It was the greatest triumph for the Bohr model that it correctly gave the value of the Rydberg constant for both hydrogen and ionized helium in terms of constants of nature measured in the laboratory.

physical consequence that the most important lines of an ionized atom lie further to the ultra-violet than those of the neutral atom. Most such lines are astrophysically inaccessible (see Appendix II), because they lie beyond 2950 A, where ozone in the Earth's atmosphere prevents observation from ground stations. Recently, however, rocket-carried spectroscopic equipment has yielded invaluable results on ultra-violet lines, and this method of research is being developed quickly.

If we excite calcium in an ordinary electric arc, we may expect lines due to the neutral atom (Ca I)[1] to appear, together with a few due to the ionized atom (Ca II). Ca I shows singlets and triplets, as does magnesium, while Ca II shows doublets. The analysis of any atomic spectrum must be preceded by a distinction between lines which belong to different stages of ionization. This can usually be achieved simply by using sources of different temperatures.

Metastable states. Comparison of figs. 10 and 12 shows one important difference between Na I and Ca II. For Ca II, the lowest D level lies slightly *below* the lowest P level, instead of above as for Na I. The transition between these two levels gives rise to three well-known strong lines in the infra-red. No transition is drawn joining the D level with the ground state, because such a D–S transition is 'forbidden' by the selection rules already mentioned.

If we now consider a Ca II ion in the D level, there is no downward transition that it can make according to the selection rules, unless it collides with another particle to which it gives up its energy of excitation. The only radiative process 'permitted' by the selection rules whereby the atom can escape from the D level is one of absorption; thus it must be raised

[1] Roman numerals following an atomic symbol are used to distinguish the various stages of ionization; I for the neutral atom, II for once ionized atoms (i.e. which have lost one planetary electron), and so on.

D

to some level of higher energy, or be ionized to Ca III. The D level is said to be *metastable* in these circumstances. From levels which are not metastable, the atom can make one or more downward transitions; and it will do so, emitting a line in the process, after only about one hundred-millionth of a second. In metastable levels the lifetime is very much longer – usually of the order of one second. The recognition of the metastable levels, if any, of each atom is of considerable importance in some astrophysical problems.

Analysis of complex spectra. The analysis of the spectrum of an atom as simple as calcium, with two valence electrons, is nevertheless one of considerable complexity, because, as we have seen, there are series of singlets and triplets, intermingled perhaps with series of doublets due to the ionized atom.

When one comes to a really complicated atom such as iron, with 8 more electrons than the closed shell of argon (the inert gas nearest to, and below, iron in the Periodic Table) it is not surprising to find that its analysis baffled investigators for a long time. In such spectra, *series* as such are no longer prominent. It is easier to recognize groups of lines; these are known as *multiplets*. The lines forming a multiplet may be considered as all arising from transitions between two levels A and B which are themselves split into sub-levels. Suppose that they are split into five levels. We write 5 as a superscript, and distinguish the sub-levels with a subscript j (the inner quantum number). Thus a quintet is formed by the group of transitions[1]

$$^{5}A_{j}-^{5}B^{0}_{j}$$

[1] In examining catalogues of multiplets or energy levels it will be noticed that some levels carry a superscript zero on the right, as does the second level in the example. Such a level is called *odd*, while others are called *even*. Transitions from even to even levels or from odd to odd are forbidden.

Selection rules restrict possible transitions between the levels to such an extent that the maximum number of lines forming a quintet is 13 instead of 25. Frequently it is still less.

Neutral atoms with odd atomic numbers have levels of even multiplicity; those with even atomic numbers have levels of odd multiplicity. This alternation law is excellently demonstrated in the group of elements from potassium to gallium, as shown below.

MULTIPLICITIES FROM K TO Ga

Neutral	K	Ca	Sc	Ti	V	Cr	Mn	Fe	Co	Ni	Cu	Zn	Ga
(Odd multiplicity)		1		1		1		1		1			
(Even multiplicity)	2		2		2		2		2		2		2
(Odd multiplicity)		3		3		3		3		3			
(Even multiplicity)			4		4		4		4				
(Odd multiplicity)				5		5		5		5			
(Even multiplicity)					6		6		6				
(Odd multiplicity)						7		7					
(Even multiplicity)							8						
Once ionized	Ca	Sc	Ti	V	Cr	Mn	Fe	Co	Ni	Cu	Zn	Ga	Ge

The table shows the multiplicity of levels of the neutral atoms listed at the top, and of the once ionized atoms at the foot.

The key to the recognition of multiplets lay in the application of Hartley's law, described earlier in this chapter, concerning constant frequency differences. Fig. 13 illustrates the principle. Four lines with frequencies a, b, c, d are associated with two upper levels and two lower levels. It is clear that

$$a - b = c - d = \text{difference between levels 3 and 4}$$
$$a - c = b - d = \text{difference between levels 1 and 2}$$

Thus if one finds pairs of lines which show the same frequency-differences more often than is to be expected by chance, one may deduce that two specific energy levels of the atom are concerned. When sufficient pairs have been found, a Grotrian diagram may be built up. Many short cuts to the successful analysis of a spectrum have been developed.

Zeeman effect. The most helpful clue to the analysis of a spectrum lies in the behaviour of the different lines when the material lies in a magnetic field. Zeeman (1896) observed that singlet lines were split, in a magnetic field, into three polarized components. This could be explained by classical theory. However, much more complicated patterns were found in the 'anomalous Zeeman effect'; these are now satisfactorily explained by quantum theory, and the type and scale of the Zeeman pattern allows one to deduce immediately the character of the levels involved (i.e. multiplicity, S, P, D series and the inner quantum number). Information on Zeeman patterns enormously restricts the number of line-pairs which need to be investigated in a search for constant frequency-differences.

We will be concerned with the Zeeman effect again later, in connection with its more direct astrophysical applications.

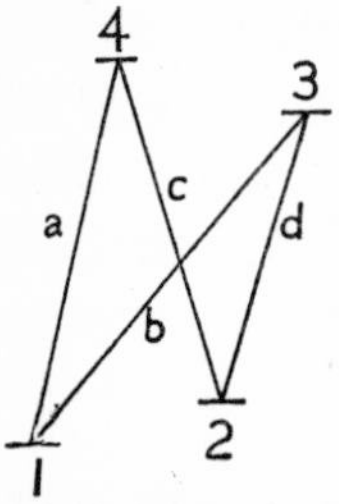

FIG. 13. Illustration of constant frequency differences.

Following the first successful analyses of complex spectra, energy levels have been derived for most atoms in the Periodic Table. As we will see, astronomical spectra have played a part and are still playing a part in such analyses.

Stark effect. Stark (1913) discovered that the Balmer hydrogen lines are split into a number of components when an element is excited in a strong electrical field. This pattern is symmetrical about the normal wavelength, and the separation increases directly with the strength of the field. The splitting of levels is of importance in quantum theory, but it does not help the analyses of spectra, and it has therefore attracted far less attention than the Zeeman effect.

Stark *splitting* of lines has not been observed in stellar spectra, because this would require *uniform* electric fields over the whole stellar atmosphere – a state of affairs which is not to be expected. However, lines in the laboratory and in stellar spectra are observed to be *broadened* by Stark effect. What happens is that in a gas containing positive ions and free electrons, any particular radiating atom may be in the strong electric field of a passing electron or ion. In the hurly-burly of colliding particles, the distances between them, and hence the strengths of the electric fields, will be varying all the time. While, therefore, we may be able to calculate what will be the average electric field in these conditions, the individual Stark patterns will be smeared out into a broadened line.

This is the explanation of the *diffuse* series (D–P) which we have already met. The Stark patterns for a given strength of field are large for this series. The splitting becomes wider along any series as we approach towards the limit. And finally, Stark effect is most pronounced for the lightest elements – hydrogen and helium – and can generally be ignored for the heavier elements.

Although Stark patterns are symmetrical for hydrogen and hydrogen-like atoms, they are not symmetrical for helium and many other more complex atoms. Consequently, Stark broadening will shift the centres of helium lines from their normal wavelengths. In the laboratory, many lines suffer shifts which increase when the pressure under which the atoms are radiating increases. This is a direct consequence of the greater strength of average electric fields between particles as the pressure increases.

Molecular spectra. Later in this book, we will have occasion to refer to molecular spectra in a few astronomical sources. Fortunately, nearly all molecules observed outside the Earth have so far been of the simplest character, consisting of only two atoms (usually both neutral). This is only to be expected because in most stars, the temperatures even at the surfaces are so high that molecules cannot survive. Thus molecular lines are seen only in the relatively cool stars, and even here the temperatures preclude the formation of molecules of any real complexity.

The spectrum of a molecule consists of *bands*, which often come to a sharp limit or head at a particular wavelength, shading off gradually on the red or blue side. The bands may be grouped in series. Examined with high power, a band is resolved into a great number of closely spaced lines.

The reason for these complexities is that a molecule can contain two additional forms of energy to those of an isolated atom. Two molecules can rotate about each other like a couple of waltzing partners. They can also approach and re-cede from each other as in a 'jiving' dance. The rotational energy is responsible for the splitting of bands into lines, while the vibrational energy is responsible for the grouping of bands into series. Either atom can absorb or emit radia-tion, as before, and change its energy level in the process. But the energy levels are broadened by the vibration and rotation of the molecule; in other words, a single spectrum line of an isolated atom is spread out into a whole series of bands when it is bound to a second atom in molecular form.

Summary. Parts of this chapter may be found rather diffi-cult reading for the non-technical student; but it will be found that everything is logical enough, and it is clear that the various problems of astronomical spectroscopy can be tackled only when the student has a thorough grasp of ele-mentary principles. It may therefore be useful to give a general summary of what has been said.

Every line in an atomic spectrum is to be attributed to a transition between two atomic states or energy levels. An absorption line corresponds to an upward transition to a state of higher energy, while an emission line corresponds to a transition to a state of lower energy. The difference in energy is proportional to the frequency of the radiation emitted or absorbed.

From the analyses of atomic spectra we find series of energy levels which converge to an ionization limit. The ionized atom gives rise to a completely new spectrum. The Grotrian diagram of the ionized atom is similar to that of the neutral atom immediately preceding it in the Periodic Table.

The Grotrian diagrams of each atom in its various stages of ionization represent permanent contributions to physical knowledge which cannot be affected by changing theories of the atom.

Magnetic and electric fields split atomic lines into Zeeman and Stark patterns respectively. The Stark effect is usually observed astrophysically in the form of broadening of lines due to varying electric fields.

Chapter 4

SPECTRA OF NORMAL STARS

The spectrum of sunlight consists of two parts, the continuous spectrum and the dark Fraunhofer lines. By analogy with Kirchhoff's experiments the continuous spectrum is commonly attributed to the hot, opaque *photosphere*, the deepest layers of the Sun to which we can see, while the Fraunhofer lines originate in the higher, cooler, levels known as the *reversing layer*.

At times when the Sun is totally eclipsed, the spectroscope shows the spectacular phenomenon of the dark lines being suddenly replaced by bright lines. Total eclipse begins when the last trace of photosphere has disappeared; for a few seconds later the upper layers of the Sun's atmosphere, known as the *chromosphere*, remain visible. From the way in which individual lines in this 'flash spectrum' fade out during these critical seconds we can study the distribution in height of the chromospheric gases above the photosphere. Roughly speaking, one may say that the chromosphere is about 10,000 km deep as judged by the strongest lines, while the reversing layer can be regarded as about 500 km deep. It must be emphasized that there is no precise boundary between photosphere, reversing layer and chromosphere. In fact, it is now realized that the distinction between photosphere and reversing layer by analogy with Kirchhoff's experiments is rather misleading.

No star except the Sun presents a visible disk. But the fact that the vast majority of stars also show continuous spectra crossed by dark lines suggests that we shall not be far wrong

56

in postulating the existence of photosphere, reversing layer and chromosphere around normal stars. In particular, when we find a star whose spectrum appears identical to that of the Sun, the structure of its atmosphere will probably resemble that of the Sun closely. The proportion of stars with peculiar spectra (e.g. in showing bright lines) is quite small.

The greater part of astrophysics is concerned with the study of the physical state of stellar atmospheres. Very broadly speaking we can approach the problem in two ways: we can concentrate on the photosphere and study the distribution of light in the continuous spectrum (avoiding absorption lines), or we can concentrate on the reversing layer and study the absorption lines. Both approaches are valuable, but owing to the complexity of line spectra more information can be extracted from them and they tend to be more actively studied than continuous spectra.

Pioneer spectroscopy. The earliest experiments in stellar spectroscopy had to be made by laborious visual methods. The two names chiefly associated with these early days are Sir William Huggins in England and Father Secchi in Italy.

Huggins was interested in identifying substances in the stars and to that end observed the brightest stars with as high dispersion as possible. He detected such familiar elements as hydrogen, iron, sodium, magnesium, calcium, etc. Secchi on the other hand was interested in comparing the spectra of as many stars as possible and classifying them in groups, just as a botanist classifies plants. His four main groups had the following features:

I. Spectra with only the lines of hydrogen visible,
II. Spectra resembling that of the Sun,
III. Spectra bearing some resemblance to that of the Sun but with bands shaded towards the red,
IV. A small group having strong bands, quite different from those of group III, shaded to the violet.

There is a close correlation of Secchi's groups with colour. The white stars (like Sirius) belong to group I, yellow stars like Capella to II, and red stars like Antares to III. The brightest star of group IV (19 Piscium) is inconspicuous to the naked eye; but it is so much redder than its neighbours, like a traffic stop light, that it is worth picking out with a small telescope.

In all Secchi classified some 4000 stars, including all naked-eye stars in the northern hemisphere. His work was followed up by Sir Norman Lockyer who, like Huggins, was interested in identifying individual substances. But Lockyer went further in comparing the behaviour of substances in the laboratory and in stars. He was well aware that certain lines of iron for instance were stronger when excited by an electric spark than by an arc; such lines, characteristic of high temperatures, he attributed to what he called 'proto-iron', and he knew that these lines were to be found among the hotter stars. Lockyer enthusiastically developed a theory (1887) of stellar evolution embracing such ideas. It was never fully accepted, but his comparison of lines in laboratory and in stars was entirely sound and his ideas of primeval atoms are very close to those of ionized atoms which are commonplace today.

As in all branches of astronomy the use of photographic plates increased enormously the efficiency of spectral classification. The permanent records could be examined at leisure freed from the risk of mistakes by a tiring observer; with long exposures stars too faint to be seen could be reached; and finally, using an objective prism many hundreds of stellar spectra could be recorded simultaneously.

The Henry Draper Catalogue. E. C. Pickering, of Harvard, took up the task with great energy. Two 8-inch telescopes, one at Harvard and the other in Peru, were used chiefly with 5° and 13° objective prisms (for faint and bright stars respectively) to record spectra of all stars in the sky down to magni-

tude 8·25 and many stars down to magnitude 10·0 and a little
fainter. The enormous task of classifying spectra of 225,000
stars was undertaken by Miss Annie J. Cannon in the years
1911 to 1914. This great Henry Draper Catalogue (published
in *Harvard Annals*, 91–100) has laid the basis for all subsequent systems of spectral classifications. While full details of
the system are to be found in the Introduction to the Catalogue, it is necessary to describe briefly the salient features
here, and especially to explain the nomenclature which has
been adopted by all astronomers.

In the Henry Draper (HD) classification the letters A, B,
etc. are used to distinguish the various spectral classes. Many
letters in the original scheme were found to be superfluous
and were therefore dropped. Instead, the remaining classes
were subdivided into tenths by the use of a number following
the letter; e.g. B5 is midway between B0 and A0. (In the HD
Catalogue gaps were left in the numbering which can be filled
in when classifying spectra of higher purity; thus, among the
F stars one will only find HD classes F0, F2, F5 and F8.) It
was found that the residual classes could be ranged in a single
sequence with a slight re-arrangement of the original alpha-
betical order. This single sequence is the following:

$$\begin{array}{c} R{-}N \\[-2pt] \diagup \\ (W){-}O{-}B{-}A{-}F{-}G{-}K{-}M \\[-2pt] \diagdown \\ (S) \end{array}$$

Ninety-nine per cent of the stars in the HD Catalogue belong
to the classes B to M, the side branches R–N and S representing rare stars. Class W has been recognized since the compila-
tion of the Catalogue. Types W to A are called 'early' and
those at the other end of the sequence 'late'.

The main features of these classes, recognizable on low
dispersion, include the following:

W   Wolf-Rayet stars, characterized by broad bright bands

of hydrogen and helium. There is some evidence of carbon and nitrogen being mutually exclusive; consequently, two sub-groups (WC and WN) are recognized.

O   Absorption due to ionized helium is found in these stars alone. Neutral hydrogen and helium are also present. Conventionally no star has been classified earlier than O5.

B   Hydrogen stronger than in O; neutral helium at its strongest in B2, disappearing in B9; lines of ionized silicon, oxygen, magnesium, etc. often visible.

A   At A0 the Balmer series of hydrogen is at its strongest, dominating the whole spectrum. The K line of Ca II increases throughout the class (from one tenth of $H\delta^1$ at A0 to three times $H\delta$ at F0).

F   H lines weakening and K line of Ca II strengthening; neutral metals strengthening.

G   The solar type. H still weakening; K very strong, numerous lines due to neutral metals. The G band (in reality a group of CH and Fe lines) is prominent. At G0 Ca I 4226 is as strong as $H\delta$.

K   Neutral metals still stronger, with H lines fading into insignificance.

M   (Secchi's group III.) Titanium oxide bands, shaded to the red, increase throughout the class. (With moderate dispersion TiO can be detected in K stars in the green or red.)

R   Intermediate between class G and N.

N   (Secchi's group IV.) Bands due to carbon compounds are characteristic of this class.

S   Characterized by bands due to zirconium oxide (in addition to titanium oxide).

---

[1] $H\delta$ refers to the fourth line in the Balmer series of hydrogen (see Plates I and II).

Stellar temperatures. The simple sequence of the Harvard classification is due to the variation of the single physical parameter – *surface temperature.* Side by side with the continuous gradation of line-patterns, there is a continuous gradation in stellar colours from the white stars of type O and B to the red stars of type K and M. The colour of a star depends primarily on the temperature of its photosphere; the colour changes from red to white in just the same way as a heated poker. Planck's law gives the intensity of 'black-body radiation' as a function of wavelength and temperature. Measurements of colour thus allow us to derive photospheric temperatures with considerable accuracy, if one assumes that stars radiate like black bodies. However, such measures have to avoid regions in the spectrum rich in absorption lines, and this is well-nigh impossible in the later types.

In the next chapter we shall see how the temperatures of reversing layers can be calculated from the behaviour of absorption lines. It is satisfactory that the results roughly parallel those derived from colours. Exact agreement is not to be expected because the two types of observation refer to different levels in a star's atmosphere, and because the radiation of many stars departs markedly from that of a black body.

By such methods Kuiper (1938) derived a stellar temperature scale, still widely used, which is partially quoted in the accompanying table on p. 62; the first two entries for the hottest stars are quoted from Petrie (1948).

Giant and dwarf stars. The table contains two columns headed giants and dwarfs for types later than F5. These terms imply knowledge of the sizes of stars and we must now explain how the spectroscope helps us to measure the radii of stars which can only be observed as points of light.

In the early Harvard work certain stars were classified with a prefix 'c' if they had very sharp clear-cut lines. Hertzsprung

THE STELLAR TEMPERATURE SCALE

Spectral Class	Temperature °K	Spectral Class	Temperature °K Giants	Dwarfs
O5	36,300	G0	5,200	6,000
B0	28,600	G5	4,620	5,360
A0	10,700	K0	4,230	4,910
A5	8,530	K5	3,580	3,900
F0	7,500	M0	3,400	—
F5	6,470	M2	3,200	3,200
		M8	2,590	—

showed that these were all very distant luminous stars emitting thousands of times as much energy as the Sun. In order to emit so much energy at a given temperature such stars must have diameters very much greater than that of the Sun. For according to Stefan's law a black body at temperature T radiates each second an amount of energy E *per unit of surface area* given by

$$E = a \times T^4$$

where a is Stefan's constant and T the temperature. The total energy emitted by a star of radius R and surface temperature T is therefore $4\pi a R^2 T^4$. Stefan's law allows us to calculate a star's radius R if we know the total energy emitted and the surface temperature. The total energy can be calculated from a star's apparent brightness if the distance is also known. The temperature T is known from the spectrum as we have seen in the preceding section.

For example, Capella A (the bright component of this close double star) has a surface temperature similar to that of the Sun while it emits about 100 times as much energy. Its radius must therefore be about 10 times that of the Sun. Canopus, radiating about 100,000 times as much energy as the Sun, is still larger. The Sun, Capella A and Canopus are therefore representatives of dwarf, giant and supergiant stars respectively. In the case of the red supergiant Antares the calculated diameter of somewhat more than 300 solar diameters has been confirmed in two ways – with an interferometer and by timing the duration of its occultation by the Moon.

Canopus and Antares are 'c' stars and the peculiarities of the spectra of these stars gave the first clue that among stars of the same spectral class (i.e. at the same temperature) there were finer details which depended upon a star's luminosity. Adams and Kohlschutter (1914) discovered certain criteria in the spectra whereby stars could be classified as giants or dwarfs. One of the most important criteria was the intensity of two lines of ionized strontium, favourably placed in that region easily photographed, which are strong in giants and supergiants. In practice, the *ratios* of certain pairs of lines are used.

Plate I shows examples of dwarfs forming the spectral sequence and Plate II shows a similar sequence of supergiants. The richness of the supergiant spectra in sharp lines, chiefly due to ionized atoms, is noteworthy.

Spectroscopic parallaxes. Adams and Kohlschutter's discovery ushered in a new era of astronomical spectroscopy because it meant that the finer details in a star's spectrum could be used to measure the star's *distance* – an achievement undreamt of in the previous century. To measure such a distance the idea of the *Absolute Magnitude* of a star is used. The absolute magnitude M of a star is defined as the apparent magnitude that it would have if it were situated at a standard distance of 10 parsecs.[1] Adams and Kohlschutter discovered how to measure M from the spectrum alone. We can measure accurately how faint the star appears at its actual distance. Then, to a first approximation, we treat space as perfectly transparent so that the apparent brightness diminishes according to the inverse square of the distance. Combination of the apparent and absolute magnitudes then yields the distance.

[1] One parsec, the unit of astronomical distances, is 3·26 light-years, or about 19 million million miles.

Just how the absolute magnitudes of stars are calibrated in terms of their spectra will be considered later (Chap. 12).

The Hertzsprung–Russell diagram. If one plots absolute

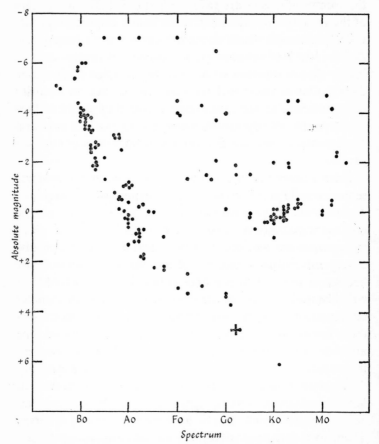

FIG. 14. HR diagram of the brightest stars in the sky. The Sun appears as the cross near the bottom of the figure.

magnitude against spectral type we have what is generally known as a Hertzsprung–Russell or *HR diagram*.

The HR diagram for all the brightest stars in the sky (down

to 3·0 apparent magnitude) is shown in fig. 14. The most striking feature of this diagram is the band of stars sloping steeply down to the right from type B to G, sharply limited on its left side. This is known as the *main sequence*. To the right and above the main sequence lie the giants with a particularly strong concentration in type K; at the top of the diagram there is a haphazard sprinkling of supergiants.

The Sun is represented by a cross at the bottom of the diagram. Only two other stars appear as faint in absolute magnitude as the Sun; they are the two bright components of the double α Centauri (the nearest star). It might therefore be concluded that the Sun is a star of exceptionally low luminosity. But the familiar naked-eye stars with which the Sun is compared in fig. 14 are familiar to us and necessarily appear bright to the naked eye just because they are stars of exceptionally *high* luminosity.

If we want a fair comparison of the Sun with other stars, we must consider all the stars that can be found in a certain volume of space centred on the Sun. In fig. 15 appears the HR diagram of all stars found within 10 parsecs of the Sun (Yale Catalogue, 1952). Here the main sequence includes nearly all the stars. But now the Sun is seen to be considerably *more luminous* than most of its neighbours. The commonest stars in our neighbourhood are M dwarfs. There must be many more stars within 10 parsecs of the Sun awaiting discovery than appear in fig. 15. This is because they are difficult to detect because they are intrinsically so faint. The least luminous star known (BD + 4° 4048 B) is of the 18th apparent magnitude; among the 100 million stars at about this level of faintness it was only picked out because it is a faint companion to a star already known to be as near the Sun as 6 parsecs.

Fig. 15 also includes a few stars well below and to the left of the main sequence. These are the *white dwarfs*. The first to

E

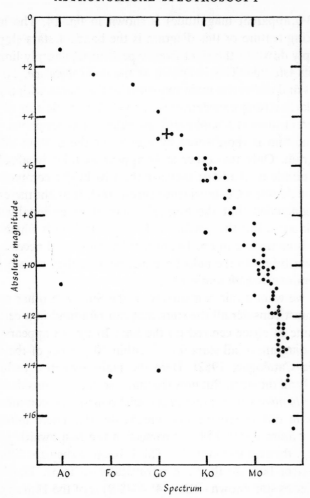

FIG. 15. HR diagram of the nearest stars. The Sun appears as the cross near the top of the figure.

be discovered (through its visual colour) was the companion of Sirius. Sirius itself is a main sequence A0 star. The companion is about 10 magnitudes fainter; if it lay on the main sequence it would be of type M and appear very strongly red compared with the white Sirius. In fact it appears just as white and is also of type A. Its high surface temperature coupled with low luminosity imply a very small surface area. The diameter derived in this way turns out to be less than three times that of the Earth.

White dwarfs are also difficult to detect but as a result of extensive searches by Luyten it seems unlikely that they are quite as abundant in space as the M dwarfs. Our knowledge of their spectra is still scanty. It is difficult to range them in a simple sequence of spectral types. Many of them show extremely broad lines – a sign of high pressure. A considerable number have been found intermediate in spectral type between A and M; for these stars of intermediate colour *white dwarf* is a misnomer, but in spite of this the term is still used for stars lying well below the main sequence.

The term *sub-dwarf* is used for stars which lie slightly below the main sequence in the HR diagram. *Sub-giants* also form an important group lying between the giants and the main sequence.

MK classification. The HD Catalogue is an invaluable guide to stellar spectroscopists and will continue so for many years to come. But it makes no distinction between giants and dwarfs; the differences were only discovered (with spectra of much superior quality) at about the time when the HD classifications were made.

In the late 1930's W. W. Morgan initiated at the Yerkes Observatory a new system of classification based on slit spectra taken with a dispersion of about 120 A/mm. The purity was sufficient to distinguish five luminosity classes denoted by Roman numerals (I for supergiants, V for dwarfs). Later work has subdivided the supergiants into first two and then four sub-groups – Ib, Iab, Ia, Ia–O (in order of increasing luminosity). Two important observational requirements

are (1) very wide spectra, (2) uniform photographic processing. A wide spectrum greatly helps to recognize faint lines,
while the processing may affect the visibility of faint outer
extensions to the lines (known as *wings*) which are an important criterion of luminosity in some spectral types.

The Morgan–Keenan–Kellman Atlas of Stellar Spectra
(1944) describes the system (MKK) in its original form with
details of the criteria for luminosity. The revised MK classification is based on a large number of standard stars. Any
observatory wishing to classify stars on this MK system
customarily compiles a set of these standard spectra with a
dispersion of about 100 A/mm.

The establishment of the MK system is the first *descriptive*
stage in a long-term programme. The second stage of determining absolute magnitudes of each luminosity class is still
the subject of extensive researches. Only a preliminary calibration has been published.

One important difference between the HD and MK classifications is that the latter depends rigorously on spectrum
lines, while among the fainter stars in the HD Catalogue the
lines were often difficult to detect and in such cases the classification was sometimes based on *colour*. This practice can
now be seen to have had unfortunate consequences:

(1) At K0, for instance, dwarfs have higher surface temperatures and are therefore bluer than giants (Table on p.
62). A true K0 dwarf judged by colour alone may be classified
as G0.

(2) Distant stars may be reddened by partial obscuration in
interstellar space (Chap. 10); such stars will be classified too
late.

The hydrogen lines play perhaps the commonest role in
classifications on low dispersion. The lines have equal intensities in B and F stars (on either side of the A0 maximum) and it occasionally happens that these two classes

are confused in consequence. Further, the extreme narrowness of the hydrogen lines in supergiants has sometimes led to gross errors in the spectral type. This emphasizes the need for a two-factor or two-dimensional system like the MK classification.

While there are many instruments in operation that could be used to improve spectral classification of stars over the whole sky and to a fainter limit than that of the HD Catalogue, no observatory has tackled such an enormous undertaking. Instead, the tendency has been to concentrate on certain areas of the sky, especially those suggested by Kapteyn and known as the Kapteyn Selected Areas, 206 in number. Hamburg, Potsdam and Stockholm Observatories among others have made important contributions in this respect.

Galactic concentration of spectral types. Recently attention has been directed chiefly to areas either in the plane of the Milky Way or in the two directions perpendicular to this plane. Stars of different types show highly significant differences in their concentration towards the plane of the Milky Way. If we count the numbers of stars per square degree (with known spectral types) in the plane of the Milky Way and well away from it, we find the following ratios for various spectral types, ratios which measure the *galactic concentration*:

Type	B2	A2	F2	G2	K2	M2
Galactic concentration	400:	55:	12	2	2	8

The first two figures are uncertain but certainly show enormously greater galactic concentration than for the other types. No distinction is made here between giants and dwarfs, but the figure for M2 type depends mainly on giants, while types F and G are largely represented by dwarfs. In general it may be stated that the stars of highest luminosity show the greatest degree of galactic concentration.

Schmidt telescopes equipped with objective prisms (e.g. in

U.S.A., Mexico, Sweden, Germany, South Africa and Australia) are recording spectra of thousands of stars per plate down to the 13th magnitude. The efficient utilization and publication of this wealth of material presents a formidable problem.

Chapter 5

IONIZATION IN STELLAR ATMOSPHERES

In the last chapter we saw that the one-dimensional sequence of spectral types in the HD classification is due to variations of the single parameter *surface temperature*. But can the striking differences in the patterns of lines shown in Plate I be explained *only* in terms of differences in temperature? And what are the reasons for the differences between spectra of dwarfs, giants and supergiants? This chapter deals, in a very elementary way, with the ionization theory, originally applied to stellar atmospheres by the Indian physicist, M. N. Saha, which to a first approximation satisfactorily answers both these questions.

A stellar atmosphere consists of a gaseous assemblage of atoms, ions and free electrons. As in the kinetic theory of gases where each constituent atom or molecule exerts a partial pressure, in a stellar atmosphere each atom, ion and free electron exerts a partial pressure proportional to the concentration of that constituent and to the absolute temperature. There is also radiation present corresponding to a certain temperature. The temperature of this radiation need not be exactly the same as the kinetic temperature of the gas, but in the present context we shall assume these temperatures to be identical.

Suppose now that we introduce a small quantity of a new constituent, which we call X, consisting entirely of neutral

71

atoms at a low temperature. Each atom X will be bombarded by particles of the original gas (at temperature T), some of which will knock off an electron from X, leaving it in the ionized state X^+. This process may be written in symbols in the form

$$X + K.E. \rightarrow X^+ + e$$

where e stands for the free electron, and K.E. for the difference in kinetic energy before and after the collision which must be absorbed in ionizing X.

Alternatively, X may absorb a quantum of radiation sufficiently energetic to ionize it. This process may be written

$$X + h\nu \rightarrow X^+ + e$$

where $h\nu$ is the energy of the quantum absorbed.

Obviously a high temperature is favourable in both these cases to ionization of X. The higher the temperature the greater is the kinetic energy content of the gas which can be drawn on in the first process; and the hotter the radiation, the richer it is in high-energy quanta required for the second process.

The amount of energy required to ionize X is the ionization potential, which as we saw in Chapter 3 can be derived from spectrum analysis. A substance like sodium with a relatively low I.P. (ionization potential) of 5·1 volts will clearly be ionized more quickly in our imaginary experiment than one like hydrogen with a relatively high I.P. of 13·5 volts. But we are not so much interested in the speed of the process of ionization as the final state of the substance X. Will all its atoms eventually become ionized or will a state of equilibrium be reached in which a definite fraction of X is ionized, and the remainder neutral?

As X becomes increasingly ionized, the partial pressure and concentration of X is steadily falling, while the partial pressure and concentration of X^+ (originally zero) is rising.

A state of equilibrium will be reached when the number of ionizations per second is exactly equal to the number of recombinations per second in the reverse process, i.e.

$$X^+ + e \rightarrow X(+\text{K.E. or } h\nu)$$

The chance of this reverse process happening is proportional to the concentration of ions X^+ and of free electrons e.

This type of problem was of course already familiar to physical chemists in discussions of dissociation or splitting up of molecular compounds. In Saha's theory, the chemical heat of dissociation is replaced by the astrophysical ionization potential.

As a final result of balancing the processes of ionization and recombination we have the ionization equation (quoted in full in Appendix IV on p. 235) which yields the ratio of concentrations of X^+ and X as a function of the three quantities

Temperature T
Electron Pressure P_e
Ionization Potential I

P_e is simply the partial pressure due to free electrons and its control of the process of recombination has been indicated.

From what has been said it will be easily appreciated that for a high degree of ionization of any substance we require high T, low P_e, low I. It is found that in the Sun's reversing layer an element with $I = 8 \cdot 0$ volts will be just half ionized, that is the concentrations of neutral and once ionized atoms will be equal; 8 volts is then the *level of ionization* of the Sun's atmosphere. An element with 6 volts I.P. or less will be heavily ionized, whereas an element like hydrogen ($I = 13 \cdot 5$) will be all neutral.

Ionization with increasing temperature: resonance lines. Let us first apply the ionization equation to the problem of calculating the proportion of neutral atoms and ions which will be present in the range of stellar temperatures at a *fixed electron pressure*.

Fig. 16 shows the ionization of calcium ($I = 6\cdot09$ volts) as a function of temperature. The full curves correspond to an assumed electron pressure of 10^{-6} atmospheres, the dashed curves to an electron pressure of $0\cdot1$ atmospheres. The curves marked I and II give the percentages of neutral and of once ionized atoms respectively.

We note first that below 3000° practically all the calcium is neutral in both cases. The percentage of Ca II ions rises with the temperature. However, for $P_e = 10^{-6}$ atm. we see

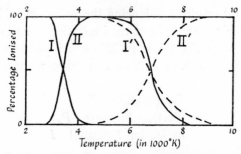

FIG. 16. Ionization of Ca. The full curves show percentage Ca I and Ca II with $P_e = 10^{-6}$ atm. The dashed curves show similar percentages with $P_e = 0\cdot1$ atm.

that the percentage of Ca II ions falls again at temperatures higher than 6000°; this is due to the second stage of ionization setting in and to an increasing concentration of Ca III ions. (The second ionization potential of Ca is 11·82 volts.)

Nearly all atoms in any stage of ionization lie in the lowest energy level from which they can absorb *resonance lines*, that is those lines which can be most easily absorbed (or most easily excited) in the laboratory. If we make the simple and reasonable assumption that the intensity of a resonance absorption line increases directly with the concentration of atoms in the appropriate stage of ionization, then we can compare the curves of fig. 16 with the observed variations of resonance lines like Ca I 4227 and Ca II H and K with spectral type. The agreement with observation is good. In the coolest stars (K and M type) Ca I 4227 is very strong (together with many lines of neutral metals) but it weakens steadily towards the earlier spectral types. The H and K lines reach a broad maximum in type G, weakening towards earlier and later types.

The most important feature of fig. 16 is the marked shift of the curves with assumed electron pressure. Since we know what temperature corresponds to each spectral type we can compare the observed behaviour of the calcium lines in stars with the curves in the diagram and find which value of the electron pressure fits best. Such a comparison shows that an assumed electron pressure of 0·1 atmosphere is too high, while a pressure of 10^{-6} atmospheres is rather low.

Until the advent of ionization theory many astronomers had expected the total gas pressure in stellar reversing layers to be about 1 atmosphere. But Saha's work showed conclusively that the pressures must be far less.

Subordinate lines. Most lines that we observe in stellar spectra are not resonance lines but arise from excited levels of the atom and are known as *subordinate lines*. The proportion of atoms in an excited level is a small one but rises with temperature according to the Boltzmann formula.[1]

The Balmer lines of hydrogen which form such an important feature in most stellar spectra are subordinate lines

[1] If N is the total number of atoms in a certain stage of ionization, the number of atoms N_1 in a particular level with energy E_1 volts is given by

$$\frac{N_1}{N} = \frac{g_1}{B(T)} \cdot e^{-\frac{E_1}{kT}} = \frac{g_1}{B(T)} \cdot 10^{-\frac{5040}{T}E_1}$$

where $B(T)$, the partition function, and g_1, the statistical weight of the level, are relatively unimportant factors compared with the exponential term. k is Boltzmann's constant.

arising from a lower level with an excitation potential of
10·15 volts. In fig. 17(*a*) the percentage concentrations of
neutral and ionized hydrogen is shown for an assumed electron pressure of 2×10^{-4} atmospheres. It will be seen that
at temperatures below 8000° K the hydrogen is essentially all
in neutral form. However, at these lower temperatures, such
a minute fraction of the H atoms will be excited to the level

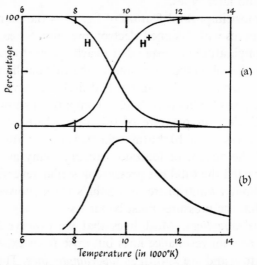

FIG. 17. (*a*) Percentage ionization of H from $T = 6000°$ to 14,000° K,
with $P_e = 2.10^{-4}$ atm. (*b*) Relative number of H atoms capable of
absorbing Balmer lines in same conditions as (*a*).

of 10·15 volts that we cannot expect the Balmer lines to be
absorbed very heavily. If we apply the Boltzmann correction
for excitation to the curve *H* of fig. 17(*a*) we have the curve
shown in fig. 17(*b*). This has a sharp maximum near
10,000° K – much sharper than the maximum for the Ca II
resonance lines in fig. 16. Subordinate lines must always
show a maximum at some temperature. Ionization theory
shows that this temperature depends upon the electron pres-

sure of the atmospheres concerned. Fowler and Milne were able to compute roughly the electron pressure in stellar atmospheres by fitting the observed maxima for a considerable number of subordinate lines to the predictions of the theory. Their results yielded electron pressures of the order of 10^{-4} atmospheres or less.

Since the Balmer lines reach their very pronounced maximum strength in stars of type A0, for which we know the temperature to be about 10,000° K, we find a fit with ionization theory for an assumed electron pressure of 2×10^{-4} atmospheres for these stars, as in fig. 17(b). By more refined methods it is possible to derive temperatures and electron pressures independently; and we now know that the electron pressure is not the same in all spectral types as assumed by Fowler and Milne.

If we could compare the relative intensities of Lyman and Balmer lines in stellar spectra, we would have a direct measure of the small proportion of H atoms excited to 10·15 volts. From the Boltzmann relation we could then derive the temperature which would be required to excite the atoms in the observed proportion, that is an *excitation temperature*. Such excitation temperatures have been measured from the relative intensities of Fe lines with excitation potentials in the range 0 to 5 volts.[1]

The criteria for spectral classification often measure the degree of ionization in a stellar atmosphere; the classification is then according to the *ionization temperature* rather than the excitation temperature. In spectral type O for instance the classification depends chiefly on the ratio of He I to He II

[1] Adams and Russell found that the excitation temperature was not the same for all lines, so that it seemed as if there might be a departure from the classical Boltzmann distribution. This result may be due to the formation of different lines at different levels in an atmosphere subject to a temperature gradient, but the matter deserves further attention.

lines, and is thus a measure of the extent to which helium is ionized in the atmosphere.

Giants and dwarfs. The ionization theory was also success-ful in explaining qualitatively some of the spectroscopic dif-ferences between giants and dwarfs. As we saw in the last chapter, dwarfs are hotter (and bluer) than giants of the same spectral class (G–K–M). If dwarf and giant stars were at the same pressure this would mean that all elements would be more heavily ionized in the dwarf. However, we would expect the pressure to be much lower in the enormously distended atmosphere of a giant. The lower pressure and temperature in the giant can just balance each other in reproducing the same degree of ionization in both giant and dwarf.

However, we must not forget the ionization potential as a third factor. It is not possible to reproduce the same degree of ionization simultaneously for all elements. As an example, the accompanying table shows the ratio of ions to neutral atoms for the elements iron and strontium at certain tem-peratures which correspond to conditions in K giants and dwarfs. The state of ionization of Fe is exactly the same in the two cases; but Sr is nearly three times as strongly ionized in the giant.

IONIZATION OF IRON AND STRONTIUM
IN K TYPE GIANTS AND DWARFS

	T $°K$	P_e $dynes/cm^2$	Ratio of ions to neutral atoms	
			Fe^+/Fe	Sr^+/Sr
Giant	3800	0·16	0·18	120
Dwarf	4500	10	0·18	42

The ionization potentials are

Fe 7·86 volts
Sr 5·67 volts

Since lines of iron (and other neutral metals having very

similar ionization potentials) dominate the observed spectra of K stars, it is the degree of ionization of iron which primarily determines the spectral classification of these stars. However, the greater intensity of the Sr II lines in giants and supergiants forms one of the most important criteria for distinguishing them from dwarfs. This can be seen by carefully comparing Plates I (dwarfs) and II (supergiants). The difference, as shown in the Table above, can be understood in terms of ionization theory.

It must be admitted that this simple example does not tell the whole story. Many more factors must be considered in the prediction of the intensity of a stellar absorption line. Few detailed comparisons of the spectra of late-type dwarfs and giants have been made and some of the differences that have been observed are not fully explained by ionization theory. As in many branches of astrophysics, it would help enormously if our observations could be extended into the far ultra-violet where the resonance lines of most of the important elements lie.

Fogginess in stellar atmospheres. For some time it was a puzzle that atmospheres with electron pressures as low as 10^{-4} atmospheres could be as opaque as they appear to be. It is not enough to consider only atoms and ions absorbing discrete lines. There must be continuous absorption as well, dimming the spectrum between the lines. The sharp edge of the Sun posed this problem in an extreme degree, for it was difficult to understand why the edge should not appear very fuzzy with a pressure of only a small fraction of an atmosphere.

Many factors are now known to contribute to continuous absorption in stellar atmospheres. These are:

(1) *Photo-electric ionization at series limits.* This is observed at the head of the Balmer series in early-type stars (see p. 43). At one time it was thought that similar ionization of metals

was an important source of opacity in late-type stars; but searches showed it to be doubtfully observable.

(2) *Free–free transitions*. A free electron passing near an ion can take up or give out kinetic energy with the emission or absorption of radiation of any wavelength; the electron remains free after such a 'side-swiping collision'.

(3) *Electron scattering*. The scattering of light by free electrons can be an important source of opacity at very high temperatures.

(4) *Negative hydrogen ions*. A hydrogen atom can capture a second electron to form H^-. The electron is very loosely bound to the atom and has an ionization potential as low as 0·5 volts. Such particles must therefore be extremely rare compared with neutral hydrogen atoms. However, hydrogen is so abundant in stellar atmospheres that Wildt was able to show that H^- ions provide the chief source of opacity (at visible wavelengths) in the Sun's atmosphere. The continuous absorption due to H^- has a very broad maximum in the infra-red.

(5) *Molecules*. In the coolest stars of all, molecules may contribute substantially to the opacity, but this problem has been little studied.

In order to explain quantitatively the intensities of lines in the spectral sequence it is essential to calculate the continuous absorption in an atmosphere at a given temperature and pressure. If the atmosphere is a foggy one with large continuous absorption, by and large all lines in the spectrum will tend to be weakened. However, an interesting situation arises when the opacity is due to one type of atom alone. Consider an atmosphere in which hydrogen is the chief source of opacity. If we double the concentration of hydrogen the opacity is doubled. All lines will therefore be weakened – all lines that is except hydrogen, for which the doubled concentration is just balanced by the increased opacity; in these circumstances we expect the hydrogen lines to remain unchanged. We thus reach the general conclusion that when the opacity is due to one element X, the intensities of lines due to X is independent of the abundance of X – up to the point where scarcity of X removes it from the position of being the chief source of opacity.

The abundances of elements and generalized ionization theory. The example just quoted shows that in order to calculate the opacity in a stellar atmosphere we must know something about the relative abundances of the commoner elements. The most important factor in the opacity is the electron pressure. There is nothing to distinguish an electron that has come from, say, a sodium, iron, hydrogen or helium atom. In the Sun the first two elements will be ionized and the latter two will be neutral. Among cooler stars the electrons come mainly from the metals, among the A type stars from hydrogen and among the still hotter stars from hydrogen and helium. Note that in the Sun the opacity is now known to be chiefly due to H^- but that the formation of this negative ion still depends upon a plentiful supply of electrons from the ionization of metals mixed with abundant neutral hydrogen.

In calculations of opacity it is usually sufficient to postulate abundances of only four elements with different mean ionization potentials: helium (24·5 volts), hydrogen (13·5 volts), and metals (8 and 6 volts).

Many calculations have been made of intensities of lines on the basis of generalized ionization theory – that is, including calculated values of the opacity. C. Payne was the first to show that in general the whole of the changing patterns of lines along the spectral sequence could be satisfactorily explained in terms of varying temperature with *a constant mixture of elements*. Generalized ionization theory also gives a better explanation of the observed differences between giants and dwarfs than the example quoted earlier.

F

The differences between the various spectral types were at one time naïvely interpreted as due to differences in stellar composition. Ionization theory showed these ideas to be unfounded. Uniformity in nature has been re-established on the wide view. A small percentage of stars are peculiar, however, and moreover the theory has till now rested on the simple assumption that the line intensity increases directly with the concentration of atoms in a state to absorb a given line. The question of peculiar abundances and of many other factors besides abundance that contribute to the intensities of lines will be taken up in a later chapter.

Chapter 6

THE DOPPLER EFFECT AND
STELLAR MOTIONS

We are all aware of the change in pitch of a whistle from an express train heard on a station platform or of the whine from passing jet aircraft. This phenomenon of sound was first explained by C. Doppler in 1842, and is commonly known as the Doppler effect. The same phenomenon occurs with light but in that context it is more properly called the Doppler–Fizeau effect, as the French physicist Fizeau corrected some erroneous ideas in Doppler's application of the principle to light.

In fig. 18 waves of light or sound are approaching a fixed

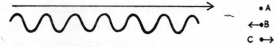

FIG. 18. The Doppler–Fizeau principle.

observer at A. The length of the arrow is supposed to represent the speed of approach (1100 ft/sec for sound, 300,000 km/sec for light). The number of waves received per second by A (that is the frequency) clearly depends on the distance between the waves or the wavelength as well as on the speed of the wave-train. A hears the note middle C when his ear receives 256 sound-waves per second; or his eye sees green when it receives 6×10^{14} light-waves per second.

Now consider B, an observer moving towards the source of sound (or light) with a speed 1 per cent of the wave-train.

83

The number of waves passing B per second will be increased by 1 per cent compared with A. Similarly for C, receding from the source, the apparent frequency will be reduced by an amount proportional to his velocity.[1]

For the phenomenon to be readily perceptible we must be dealing with a fairly pure tone in sound or pure colour in light. A noise, or a pure white body radiating all wavelengths equally, will not work. Now stars are light-sources that can be termed 'noisy' in that their light consists of a rich and fairly uniform blend of all colours from ultra-violet to infra-red. This is where Doppler made his mistake, for he thought that the range of stellar colours from blue to red was due to motions of the stars towards and away from us (and not, as we now know, to different temperatures). Such changes in apparent colour due to motion could occur physically, but would involve very much higher velocities than are found in the Galaxy.

Fizeau showed great foresight in pointing out, before the significance of the Fraunhofer lines was understood, that the positions of these Fraunhofer lines in the spectrum would be shifted by amounts proportional to the relative velocity of the star in the line of sight (*the radial velocity*). The dark lines in a star's spectrum give us accurate markers of pure colours (or rather absence of pure colours); their positions can be measured with considerable accuracy relative to some terrestrial standard and we can thus measure the star's velocity relative to this standard. Practically every star in the sky shows some lines in its spectrum from which its radial velocity can be determined.

[1] In mathematical form the Doppler–Fizeau principle states that if a source of monochromatic wavelength λ_0 is viewed by an observer moving towards the source with a relative velocity v, then the apparent wavelength will be $\lambda = \lambda_0 (1 + v/c)$, where c is the velocity of light. The relation breaks down when v becomes very large, comparable with c.

Measurement of radial velocities. Attempts to measure radial velocities were made by several visual observers (notably Sir William Huggins). But accuracy was hard to attain. The introduction of photography was a great step forward, but even then the shifts to be measured were so small that they were often masked by instrumental errors.

For instance, in the blue part of the spectrum a velocity of 1·0 km/sec corresponds to 0·014 A. Even at the rather high dispersion (for stellar spectroscopy) of 10 A/mm the corresponding linear shift to be measured on the photographic plate amounts to only 0·0014 mm. A sharp line can be measured in a microscope to this accuracy (or at any rate the average of a number of lines). An accuracy of 1·0 km/sec in radial velocities is attainable for the bright stars.

However, an exposure lasting several hours is often required to obtain the spectrum of a star with adequate dispersion. During this time the spectrograph attached to the moving telescope will change its position relative to the vertical. In such conditions any change in the bending or flexure of the spectrograph under gravity may have disastrous effects upon the minute Doppler shifts that the observer tries to measure.

Similarly, a change in temperature of the spectrograph during a long exposure may produce equally disastrous instrumental errors. For instance, a change of 1° C in a prism spectrograph (with flint glass) will produce a shift corresponding to about 40 km/sec. Stellar spectrographs are therefore almost invariably provided with temperature control.[1] Moreover it is regular practice to photograph the terrestrial standard at beginning and end (and sometimes in the middle) of

[1] It is of interest that the control only needs to provide for falling temperatures during the night. On the rare occasions when the temperature rises during the night clouds usually form and prevent further observation!

the exposure on the star; this procedure largely eliminates residual effects of temperature changes.

Given a temperature-controlled spectrograph free from appreciable flexure, what is the procedure for measuring the radial velocity of a star? On either side of the spectrum of the star, the spectrum of some standard terrestrial source (e.g. the iron arc) is photographed (see top and bottom of Plate II). This comparison spectrum fixes a scale of wavelengths on the plate (at rest relative to the observer).[1] The measured position of any one line in the spectrum of the star can now be transformed into this scale of wavelengths. Knowing the laboratory wavelength (λ_{lab}) of such stellar lines, we calculate the shift $\lambda-\lambda_{lab}$ for all suitable stellar lines, and hence the corresponding velocity from the Doppler–Fizeau relation. The resulting mean velocity is the measured radial velocity of the star *relative to the observer at the time of observation*. The Earth has an orbital velocity of about 30 km/sec around the Sun; the component of this velocity towards the star has to be removed in order to yield the more fundamental measure of the velocity *relative to the Sun*. A much smaller correction which takes account of the rotation of the Earth is also required for precise measures.

Astronomical confirmation of the Doppler effect. The shifts of spectrum lines proportional to velocity and wavelength have been observed in the laboratory (1900) but confirmation of the principle came from astronomical sources many years before this.

It was known from observations of sunspots that the Sun

---

[1] For a prism spectrograph the Hartmann–Cornu formula gives the following relation between the horizontal position on the plate (n) and wavelength (λ):

$$n - n_0 = \frac{c}{\lambda - \lambda_0}$$

where n_0, c and λ_0 are constants.

rotates in a period of about 25 days. The Sun's radius being 0·7 million km, the equatorial velocity should be 2·0 km/sec. The spectroscope did indeed show shifts to red and violet on opposite sides of the Sun of the correct size, and proportional to wavelength, in full confirmation of the principle. In passing it may be noted that although the shift corresponding to 2·0 km/sec is rather small in stellar spectroscopy, it becomes quite accurately measurable with the powerful spectroscopes that can be employed on the solar spectrum.

Similarly, rotation of some planets was observed spectroscopically in agreement with that deduced from surface markings.

Motions of the planets around the Sun are known with very great accuracy from classical astronomy. The components of these motions towards or away from the Earth were also found to agree perfectly with those deduced from spectroscopic shifts. In the case of the Earth itself we have already mentioned the necessity to correct a star's apparent motion for the component due to the Earth's orbital motion around the Sun. Without applying this correction we would find that the radial velocities of all stars would seem to vary through the year; for stars on the ecliptic the variation amounts to 60 km/sec. This phenomenon provides another direct proof of the Doppler effect.

Early applications of the Doppler effect. (a) *Saturn's rings.* When the slit of a spectroscope is placed along Saturn's equator crossing the rings, the spectrum lines present a zig-zag appearance as in fig. 19. The ball of the planet shows sloping lines in accordance with the rotation known from the rare appearance of cloud markings, a shift to the left (violet) indicating approach. The parts of the rings nearest to the planet on the approaching side show a larger shift to the violet; the rings therefore rotate in the same sense as the planet. The outer parts of the rings also rotate but *at a slower rate* than the inner. The rings therefore do not rotate like a solid body; just as for the planets in the solar system, the angular velocity decreases towards the outer parts.

Keeler's observation of this phenomenon was a brilliant confirmation of a brilliant mathematical calculation by Clerk Maxwell, who proved that owing to tidal forces the rings must be composed of separate moonlets moving more rapidly in the inner than the outer parts of the rings.

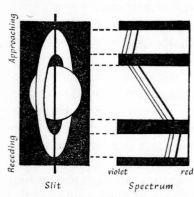

FIG. 19. Spectroscopic signs of the rotation of Saturn and its rings.

(b) *Spectroscopic binaries.* The spectra of some bright stars were soon discovered to show periodic doubling of lines. These were recognized as pairs of stars moving around each other, too closely to be resolved by the telescope.[1]

Two conditions are necessary for the recognition of two spectra in a spectroscopic binary: (1) the maximum difference in radial velocity must be great enough for the lines to be resolved. If a binary system should be moving in an orbit in the plane of the sky there will be no change in radial velocity and we cannot hope to recognize such a system; (2) the difference in brightness of the two stars must not be too great, otherwise only one spectrum will be observed.

However, many stars show a single spectrum with regu-

[1] Double stars resolved by the spectroscope through varying radial velocities are known as spectroscopic binaries. In some cases two stars can be recognized even without Doppler shifts; *composite spectra* are sometimes observed, for example at the red end of the spectrum we can recognize a red star of type K, while in the blue we see a star of type A.

larly varying radial velocity. These are single-line spectro-scopic binaries. In most cases we can be sure that a second star is present, too faint to be observed.

(c) *Visual binaries.* Great numbers of pairs of stars are observed in the telescope moving around each other in periods of tens or hundreds of years. Such visual binaries are usually separated from each other by distances much greater than those of the spectroscopic binaries; their relative speeds are correspondingly *small*, and in most cases the spectroscope shows no measurable difference in their radial velocities. In a few favourable cases, especially the nearest star, α Centauri, the difference is measurable.

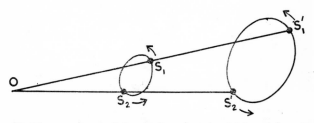

Fig. 20. The varying radial velocity of a visual binary fixes it at a certain distance.

Fig. 20 shows such a system viewed from the Earth at *O*. The telescope shows the stars S_1, S_2 separated by a certain angle at a particular time and revolving around each other in a certain period (80 years for α Centauri). From gravita-tional theory we know that the stars must be moving in ellipti-cal orbits in a certain plane. From an accurate orbit in the sky we can work out how the plane of the true orbit is in-clined to the plane of the sky. We can now combine the telescopic measures of cross-motions with the spectroscopic measures of radial velocity in a powerful way. The telescope by itself measures changes of angles with time. Without other evidence the stars might just as well be twice as far off, at

S'_1, S'_2 in the figure; but since the orbit has to be completed in a definite time, the speeds of the stars would then be twice as great at the greater distance. If therefore we know the radial velocities of the stars (in km/sec) we can calculate at what distance the stars must be to render the velocities consistent with the visual orbit.

Solar motion. There are many other examples of the power of combining telescopic measures of cross-motions with spectroscopic measures of radial velocity.

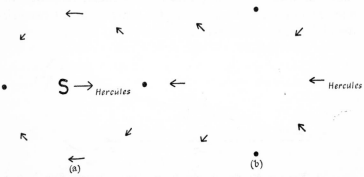

FIG. 21. Solar motion. (*a*) Proper motions: the stars in their cross-motions appear to drift away from Hercules. (*b*) Radial velocities: the spectroscope shows that stars in the constellation Hercules are approaching the Sun; those in the opposite hemisphere are receding.

William Herschel noticed that the few stars whose cross-motions were known in his day – there were only 13 of them – seemed to be drifting away from the constellation Hercules. He correctly guessed that this was due to the Sun itself, together with the rest of the solar system, moving towards Hercules relative to the nearby stars. The drift is of course most obvious in those parts of the sky 90° from Hercules (see fig. 21*a*).

Herschel's guess was fully confirmed by radial velocities. The spectroscope shows that stars in the direction of Hercules tend to approach us, while those in the opposite direction are moving away from us; on the average no radial velocity is observed for nearby stars along the great circle where the cross-motions are largest (fig. 21b).

The importance of the radial velocities was not only in confirming the *direction* of the solar motion, but in fixing its amount as about 20 km/sec. The actual speed could not be determined from the proper motions alone without knowing the distances of the stars. We shall revert to this problem in a later chapter dealing with methods of measuring stellar distances.

All motion is relative, and this solar speed of 20 km/sec is what we call the Sun's *peculiar motion* relative to the nearby stars. We now know that the group of nearby stars including the Sun has a high speed relative to other parts of the Milky Way.

High-velocity stars. We find that most of the stars in our neighbourhood resemble the Sun in having peculiar motions of about 20 km/sec. A natural question to ask is whether the motions of the stars are similar to those of molecules in a gas. Compare, for instance, the mean speed of 2 km/sec for hydrogen molecules at room temperature.

In a gas the distribution of velocities follows Maxwell's law and no directions are preferred over others. In the motions of stars preferred directions are the rule, and many more stars are found with velocities greater than 60 km/sec than would be expected from Maxwell's law. Such stars have assumed considerable importance in recent years. Probably the motions of these high-velocity stars have been determined by causes different from those controlling the motions of the Sun and other low-velocity stars.

It was soon found that the high-velocity stars have a strong tendency to approach us from the direction of the constellation Cygnus. In and near that constellation the radial velocities of the high-velocity stars are nearly always negative, while they are positive in the opposite side of the sky.

The explanation of this peculiar phenomenon came from the study of the motions of stars at a considerable distance from the Sun. These stars could only be studied satisfactorily with the spectroscope through the Doppler effect.

Galactic rotation. The Sun, thought at one time to be near the centre of our Galaxy, is now known to be far from the true centre. The flattened form of the Milky Way suggests that the Galaxy itself is in rapid rotation.

In the outer parts of a rotating Galaxy the motions are likely to be controlled by a central mass, just as the motions of the planets are controlled by the gravitation of a central Sun. In these circumstances the angular velocity should decrease outwards from the centre (cf. Saturn's rings).

In fig. 22a *S* represents the Sun and *C* the centre of the Galaxy. The arrows represent motions of the Sun and fairly distant stars relative to the centre. The inner parts with longer arrows have the higher velocities.

Fig. 22b shows the same motions *relative to the Sun*, in the line of sight. The spectroscope should show velocities of approach in the directions *SA*, *SA'*, if the Galaxy rotates in this way, because *A* is catching up the Sun which in turn is catching up *A'*. Similarly, positive velocities of recession are to be expected in directions *B*, *B'*. In the four intermediate directions marked by dots there should be no component of radial velocity. The radial velocities of B type stars observed by Plaskett and Pearce at Victoria, Canada, brilliantly confirmed these expectations and proved conclusively that the Galaxy near the Sun is subject to differential rotation. The effect is best illustrated in the form of fig. 23. Here we plot the average radial velocity of various parts of the Milky Way against galactic longitude (that is, the various directions from

S in fig. 22*b*. At *B*, *B'* in fig. 23 positive velocities (recession) are found, corresponding to the directions *B*, *B'* in fig. 22*b*. Similarly negative velocities (approach) are found in directions *A*, *A'*.

Proper motions also show similar variation with galactic longitude, due to the galactic rotation, but the observations

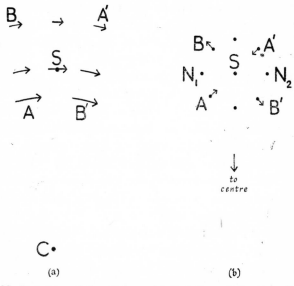

FIG. 22. Rotation of the Galaxy. (*a*) Rotation of the Sun (*S*) and nearby stars relative to the centre (*C*). (*b*) Radial velocities of the stars relative to the Sun in a rotating galaxy.

are difficult. Further, radial velocities have one enormous advantage over proper motions in this problem. The amplitude of the curve of fig. 23 *increases with the distance of the star*; in proper motions the amplitude remains the same at all distances. In nearly every astrophysical problem observational difficulties increase as one reaches further out into space. In studying galactic rotation through the measurement of radial velocities of distant stars, the difficulties associated with observing faint distant stars are largely offset by the fact that the velocities to be measured are larger.

To quote numerical examples, an 8th magnitude early B type star will lie at a distance of about 1 kiloparsec from us. At this distance the curve of galactic rotation has an amplitude of 17 km/sec, an easily detectable quantity. Supergiants of 8th and 9th magnitude lie at much greater distances, and

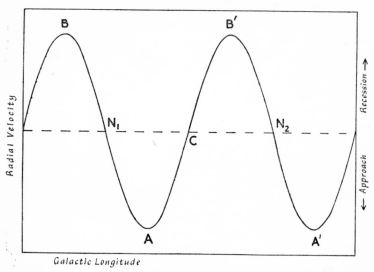

FIG. 23. Galactic rotation observed in radial velocities of distant stars.

observed radial velocities of over 50 km/sec due to galactic rotation are not unknown.

The distance and direction to the centre of the Galaxy. The four points in fig. 23 where the radial velocity is zero are called nodes. The node *C* corresponds to the direction to the centre of the Galaxy. The direction found from the radial velocities agrees closely with that independently suggested by the distribution of globular clusters and by other arguments.

This direction lies in the constellation Sagittarius where there are exceptionally rich star clouds.[1]

The two nodes N_1, N_2 have special importance because as greater distances are reached the simple sine-wave curve of fig. 23 is distorted in such a way that these nodes are shifted towards C. This shift can be used to measure the distance of the Sun from the centre of the Galaxy. In fig. 24 N_1, N_2 represent two stars at a distance r (supposed known) from the Sun and at the same distance R_0 from C as the Sun. We assume that these stars have the same circular velocity V about C as the Sun. They will there-fore have zero radial veloc-ity relative to the Sun; thus they must lie in the direc-tions of the two nodes N_1, N_2 of fig. 23. Clearly as one increases the radius r of the circle centred on S (that is as one observes more dis-tant stars) the nodes N_1, N_2 will shift towards the direction SC. From the

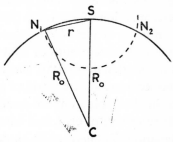

FIG. 24. Determination of the dis-tance from the Sun to the centre of the Galaxy from radial velocities.

geometry of the isosceles triangle SN_1C (in which the angle CSN_1 and the side SN_1 are known) we can easily determine the unknown SC, that is the distance to the centre.

If we know the circular velocity of the Sun round the centre and the distance to the centre, Newtonian mechanics allows us to measure the mass of the stars concentrated towards the centre that is responsible for the observed rotation. Although the existence of differential galactic rotation is very well

[1] The direction to the centre has been determined recently with great accuracy by radio observations. The centre itself appears to be an extra-ordinarily strong source of radio waves.

established, the actual velocity of the Sun around the centre and the distance R_0 are still both known quite roughly. According to our present knowledge it may be stated approximately that

Distance, Sun to centre   =   9 kiloparsecs
Sun's velocity around centre = 220 km/sec
Period of Sun's rotation   = 250 million years
Mass of Galaxy   = 2×10^{11} Suns

Many more observations are required to strengthen these results. One of the greatest needs is to improve the accuracy of determination of all stellar distances.

Motions of globular clusters. Globular clusters are spectacularly dense groups of faint stars, of which 118 have been recognized in the Galaxy. Their radial velocities are very large and seem to indicate a drift of about 170 km/sec past the Sun in the direction from the node N_2 of fig. 24. This is exactly the same sort of drift, and from the same direction (the constellation Cygnus), as is shown by the high-velocity stars already mentioned. In the light of the picture of galactic rotation just discussed the behaviour of the globular clusters and of the high-velocity stars is clear. *They do not partake in the general rotation of the Galaxy,* or if they do, much less so than the Sun. We have quoted the figure of 220 km/sec for the Sun's approximate speed of rotation; the observed backward drift of 170 km/sec shown by the globular clusters would then mean that there is only 50 km/sec left over for their rotation around the centre (in the same sense as the Sun). The term 'high-velocity' is a misnomer when one considers motion relative to the galactic centre.

Fig. 25 represents a schematic side-view of the galaxy, most of the bright stars, including the Sun S, being enclosed within the full curve (I). Other objects, like the globular clusters and high-velocity stars, are found in more nearly spherical volumes like those marked II, well away from the plane of the Milky Way.

Motions and distribution in the Galaxy. When we group stars according to physical characteristics we find that there is a very general relation between the degree of flattening to the Milky Way plane and their velocity of rotation. The curves I and II (fig. 25) are extreme examples of this. The situation is a close parallel of that in the solar system where the planets, with roughly circular motion, are confined to the plane of the ecliptic, while the comets with strongly elliptic

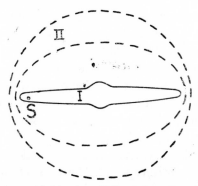

FIG. 25. Schematic side-view of the Galaxy. The Sun is at *S*.

orbits have strong inclinations to the ecliptic. Similarly, globular clusters and high-velocity stars have elliptic orbits in the Galaxy; the high inclinations of these orbits to the plane of the Milky Way mean that they are mostly found well out of that plane, i.e. with little or no galactic concentration.

The following table shows examples of the relation between the galactic concentration and solar motion *V* of various physical groups. Here it must be remembered that small values of *V* imply a high velocity of galactic rotation, and vice versa.

G

CORRELATION OF SOLAR MOTION AND GALACTIC CONCENTRATION OF PHYSICAL GROUPS

Group	V (km/sec)	Galactic Concentration
B0–B5	20	very strong
G giants	13·5	strong
G dwarfs	30	weak
M variables		
period > 300d	16	average
period < 300d	58	none
Subdwarfs	153	none
RR Lyrae variables	130	none
Globular clusters	170	none

This correlation between motion and physical characteristics is one of the sensational results of the labours of many observers in accumulating radial velocities of stars.

Objective prism velocities. The number of stars in the Galaxy with measured radial velocities now exceeds 20,000, including every star in the sky with apparent magnitude $5\frac{1}{2}$ or brighter. Most of them have been measured one at a time with slit spectrographs. Fehrenbach has successfully developed the technique whereby radial velocities can be measured on objective prism spectra. This means that (just as with spectral classification) two hours' work at the telescope with an objective prism may yield velocities of over 100 stars instead of the velocity of only one with a slit spectrograph. The accuracy is generally lower than that obtained with slit spectra, but nevertheless the technique is yielding data of great statistical importance and its wider use is greatly to be desired. For many years radial velocity work has been pursued much more intensively in the north than in the south; consequently the number of southern stars with known velocities is only about one quarter that of the northern stars.

The Doppler shifts that we have been discussing refer mostly to the motions of whole stars within the Galaxy.

Further applications of the Doppler effect will however be found in later chapters in which we shall be concerned with motions within a stellar atmosphere, in the regions of space between us and the stars, or in those still more distant regions outside our own particular Galaxy.

Chapter 7

THE SPECTRA OF THE SUN
AND PLANETS

The Sun, as the nearest star, has three obvious advantages for the astronomical spectroscopist. There is, for once, so much light available that very high dispersion can be used to reveal fine details in the spectrum. Secondly, we can isolate portions of the Sun's surface with a spectrograph-slit, to study the nature of sunspots or to analyse the Sun's atmosphere by comparing the centre of the disk with the edge or *limb*. Finally, by a fortunate accident the Moon is situated at just the right distance to cover up neatly the Sun's disk at times of eclipses; on such occasions the spectroscope tells us about the physical nature of the Sun's uppermost layers, the chromosphere and corona.

The continuous spectrum of the Sun. A direct view of the Sun, without a spectroscope, shows that the surface appears brighter at the centre than near the edge. This *darkening to the limb* can be profitably studied with the spectroscope in different colours, care being taken to measure the continuous spectrum between absorption lines. The darkening is more pronounced at the shorter wavelengths for a reason that can be easily appreciated. Near the limb we look tangentially through a foggy atmosphere; consequently our view is blocked at a higher level in the Sun's atmosphere than when we view the centre of the disk. The limb is redder than the centre simply because at these higher levels the temperature
100

is lower. From accurate measures of the limb-darkening we can measure the temperature gradient in the Sun's atmosphere.

Another important observational datum is the spectral energy curve of the radiation from the centre of the disk. Again great care must be taken to avoid regions of absorption lines. The curve shows marked deviations from that corresponding to black-body radiation. For instance, from 4000 A (where the curve reaches its maximum intensity) to 5000 A the centre of the disk radiates like a black body at temperature 7100° K, but in the ultra-violet from 3200 to 3700 A it radiates like a black body at temperature 5780° K.

Combination of measures of limb-darkening and of the spectral energy curve at the centre of the disk allows us to measure the temperature, pressure, continuous absorption, and the variation of these quantities with depth in the atmosphere. Further, such measures have shown that the continuous absorption is *not* the same at all wavelengths but that it varies with wavelength in a manner predicted for negative hydrogen ions. This is the chief evidence that negative hydrogen ions provide most of the opacity in the atmospheres of the Sun and of the cooler stars.

Besides the limb-darkening, the continuous spectrum shows local variations in intensity – most marked of all in the dark sunspots. Measures of bright areas known as *faculae* indicate that their temperatures are probably 100° K higher than those of surrounding regions. Their greater visibility towards the limb indicates an origin high in the atmosphere. Much smaller bright areas, only about 500 miles across, known as *granulation* appear all over the Sun with such contrast as indicates temperatures 100–200° higher than the photosphere. The granulation changes perpetually, individual granules being detectable for only 3 minutes at a time. Spectroscopic examination of such transient features is exceedingly difficult but measures of Doppler shifts have been achieved which show them to be the top of hot mushroom-like eruptions from the lower levels, rising with average speeds of 0·4 km/sec.

Chromosphere, reversing layer and sunspots. The 'flash' spectrum of the chromosphere consists of bright lines, while the reversing layer shows only dark lines on a continuous background. At first sight the chromospheric bright lines seem to match the dark Fraunhofer lines rather well. Closer inspection shows that certain lines are much stronger in the chromosphere, particularly those of ionized iron and titanium; the most spectacular case is provided by helium[1] which is strong in the chromosphere but does not appear in the Fraunhofer spectrum. Since Fe II, Ti II and He I require a high temperature for their appearance, it looked as though the Sun's atmosphere must grow hotter as one proceeded upwards into the higher levels of the chromosphere. This paradoxical situation was largely solved by ionization theory.

The ionization of Fe and Ti in the chromosphere is due to *low pressure*. The comparison between reversing layer and chromosphere is similar to that between a dwarf G star and a giant. However, helium presents a more difficult problem: ionized helium is weakly present in the chromosphere, varying from point to point. To explain the ionization of helium we would require a temperature of order 20,000° as compared with 5000° for the ionization of the metals. In conditions like those of the chromosphere departures from thermodynamic equilibrium may be expected; temperatures may take widely different values depending on how they are defined. The ionization of helium could be produced by bursts

---

[1] Discovered in the chromosphere at the eclipse of 1868 and so called from the Greek word *hēlios* (sun), because it was not recognized on the Earth. A quarter of a century later, however, it was isolated in a laboratory, and identified spectroscopically with the solar gas.

of extreme ultra-violet radiation from 'hot spots', radiation to which the metals would be far less sensitive.

Quantitative analysis of the chromospheric spectrum is difficult because the chromosphere is viewed tangentially and the gas is sufficiently thick to cause the strongest lines to be weakened by the process of self-absorption.[1]

Sunspots are cool regions compared with their surroundings. They only appear dark because the radiation is less from such cool regions in accordance with Stefan's law. The lower temperature is beautifully shown in a comparison of disk and spot spectra. Lines of neutral atoms strengthen in the spot, those of ionized atoms weaken, and the temperature is low enough for molecules like TiO to appear.

The ionization potential of lithium (5·37 volts) is so low that this element is completely ionized, so that its characteristic neutral line can scarcely be observed in the disk, while its ionized lines lie too far in the ultra-violet to be observed. However, at the lower temperature of sunspots, the concentration of neutral atoms is strong enough for the line to be seen.

The Fraunhofer spectrum of the disk. Outside regions of sunspots the pattern of Fraunhofer lines remains remarkably constant, although there are minor but important changes towards the limb. The great *Revised Rowland Table of Solar Wavelengths* (1928) lists 20,027 lines in the range 2975 to 7330 A with an appendix of 1808 lines extending to 10,218 A. Still further extensions to the infra-red have been possible subsequently. In very recent years the barrier of ozone absorption at 2975 A has been penetrated by spectrographs carried on high-altitude rockets.[2]

[1] In the laboratory it is common to find strong emission lines with a central core of absorption.

[2] In the far ultra-violet these rocket spectra have revealed a wealth of *emission lines*, of which Lyman α (1215 A) is easily the strongest;

A new and greatly enlarged version of the *Revised Rowland Catalogue* is in preparation. But it is useful to describe certain features of the Catalogue, and in particular to explain the principles underlying the identification of lines with various elements. The same principles govern the procedure of identification in all stellar spectra.

The Catalogue lists accurate wavelengths (to an accuracy of 0·001 A) and visual estimates of intensity in both disk and spot. In order to identify a particular line, satisfactory agreement with an observed laboratory wavelength is a prime necessity, but by itself is not sufficient. The change from disk to spot must agree with the predictions of ionization theory. Moreover, the intensity in the disk itself can be predicted roughly if other stronger lines of the same element have already been found.

Given a particular atom whose spectrum has been analysed, the first step is to see whether it has an ultimate line represented in the accessible solar spectrum. If apparently present, other strong lines due to the same atom are sought, to test whether this is chance coincidence. If absent, the ionization potential is examined to see whether the atom is only likely to be present in ionized form; the strongest ionized lines are then sought.

In the Catalogue, the commonest identifications are with iron (3288 lines), titanium (1085 lines) and chromium (1028 lines). This of course is evidence of the richness of the spectra of these atoms rather than of great abundance. Over 1000 solar lines have been attributed to iron, on very sound grounds, which *have never been observed in the laboratory*;

R. Tousey and his colleagues have identified these bright lines with H, He, C, N, O, Al, Si, S, P and Fe in various stages of ionization of which the highest is O VI (*Ap. J.* **127**, 80, 1957). They have also succeeded in photographing the Sun's surface in Lyman α light (*Sky and Telescope*, June 1959, p. 441).

the wavelengths are predicted by analysis of energy levels, and conditions in the Sun's atmosphere are more favourable to their appearance than in the laboratory.

The strongest lines are due to calcium, hydrogen and iron. Again, this is not necessarily a sign of great abundance. The resonance lines of calcium and iron lie at wavelengths easily observed; the resonance lines of many lighter elements (now known to be more abundant) lie in the inaccessible ultra-violet.

When an element like iron is known to be represented by many strong lines, one proceeds to examine each known multiplet in turn. As one proceeds to the weaker multiplets one will find only the strongest members represented. Identifications of weak lines naturally have to be made with great care. A great many solar lines are due to unresolved blends of two or more lines, and consideration of intensities of related lines in multiplets helps us to gauge the relative importance of various contributors.

In the Catalogue as much as 43 per cent of all the lines listed are left unidentified. These are mostly weak lines and it has been suggested that the majority of them are due to molecules.

The current position in regard to identification of the 92 elements up to uranium is summarized in the accompanying table (p. 106).

We know with certainty of the existence of 67 elements in the Sun, a considerable advance on the 40 or so identified by Rowland (1897). A large proportion of elements listed as absent in the table have no ultimate lines accessible; in this group the lower excitation potential of accessible lines ranges from 4·9 volts for Hg to 16·6 volts for Ne; and with such excitations such a small proportion of the atoms will be able to absorb the lines that their appearance is not surprising. Note in particular the high E.P. for Ne; neon is known to be

ELEMENTS IN THE SUN

Present – no comment	H, He, Be, C, N, O, Na, Mg, Al, Si, P, S, K, Ca, Sc, Ti, V, Cr, Mn, Fe, Co, Ni, Cu, Zn, Ga, Ge, Sr, Y, Zr, Nb, Mo, Ru, Rh, Pd, Ag, Sn, Sb, Ba, La, Ce, Pr, Nd, Sm, Eu, Gd, Dy, Tm, Yb, Lu, Hf, W, Os, Ir, Pt, Pb	55
Evidence from sunspot spectrum	Li, Rb, In	3
Present in compounds only	B, F	2
Only one line present	Ar,* Cd, Au, Th	4
Present?	Tb, Er, Ta	3
	Total present	67
Indeterminate	As, Tc	2
Insufficient laboratory data	Pm, Ho	2
Absent: Ultimate lines accessible	Cs, Re, Tl, Bi, Ra, U	6
Ultimate lines inaccessible	Hg, Te, Se, I, Br, Xe, Cl, Kr, Ar,* Ne*	9
	Total absent	15
Not to be expected	Po, At, Rn, Fa, Ra, Ac, Pa, and transuranian elements	

* Argon is represented by one 'forbidden' line in the solar corona. Ultraviolet neon emission has been found in rocket spectra (1960).

Courtesy Charlotte E. Moore, *Science*, **113**, 672, 1951.

a cosmically abundant element from observations of nebulae. The only reason why no neon lines are found in the solar spectrum is because there are no suitable lines in the accessible region of wavelengths. A similar situation occurs with argon, but here there is one suitable line which appears in the peculiar spectrum of the corona.

It is of interest that the elements boron and fluorine are only found in molecular form.

Relativity shift. Very accurate measures of wavelength of the Fraunhofer lines in the Sun reveal minute discrepancies compared with laboratory wavelengths. Einstein's theory of relativity predicted a shift to the red of all lines in the spectra of Sun and stars. This is because every quantum of radiation must, according to the theory, lose some energy in escaping from the Sun's gravitational field. The shift is proportional to wavelength and is therefore indistinguishable from a velocity shift. The solar red shift, with predicted value 0·6 km/sec, is of about the same size as that due to random atmospheric motions. In comparing solar and laboratory wavelengths account must also be taken of shifts due to atomic collisions, which vary from line to line.

The observed red shift in the solar spectrum agrees as well as can be expected with the predictions of relativity at the limb of the Sun (after allowing of course for the shift due to rotation) but at the centre of the disk it is smaller, and different for different lines. There is an unexplained correlation of the shifts with the intensities of the lines. Attempts to explain the variation from centre to limb in terms of atmospheric motions have not been entirely successful.[1]

Atmospheric lines. From the yellow through red to infrared many lines appear which are due to absorption in the Earth's atmosphere and not in the Sun. This is proved in two ways:

(1) the lines strengthen as the Sun sinks to the horizon and

---

[1] Some observational confirmation of the predicted red shift is found in two white dwarfs. But the observations are very difficult. Einstein's predictions do seem to be confirmed by recent laboratory experiments (*Nature*, **185**, 653, 1960).

its rays pass through increasingly thick layers of the Earth's atmosphere;

(2) the lines do not show the Doppler shifts due to the Sun's rotation.

The second point is occasionally important in problems of identification. For instance, an important line of potassium is completely masked by an atmospheric line in the spectrum of the centre of the solar disk. However, by observing the east or west limb of the Sun, the rotational shift brings the solar line into view.

Magnetic fields and motions in sunspots. In Chapter 2 reference was made to the spectroheliograph, an instrument which can be 'tuned in' to wavelengths of certain absorption lines, especially hydrogen or ionized calcium. These monochromatic images of the Sun show glowing clouds over the surface, particularly in the neighbourhood of sunspots. Hale noticed vortical patterns around sunspots on these images. The apparent rotational motions of charged particles suggested that sunspots might be the source of magnetic fields. Hale searched successfully for Zeeman splitting of lines in sunspot spectra and measured fields up to 3000 or 4000 gauss.

It is curious that the vortical patterns round spots which led to Hale's great discovery are apparently *not* connected with the magnetic fields. Statistically, the sense of the vortices follows a law like that of cyclones in the northern and southern hemispheres of the earth. The spectroheliograph shows high-level phenomena, probably dominated by hydrodynamic circumstances.

The dominant motion in the lower levels of sunspots is *radial*. Evershed discovered Doppler shifts indicating that lower gases are pouring outwards from spots parallel to the Sun's surface, while the uppermost flow inwards.

A satisfactory model for all the observed features of sunspots has still to be proposed.

Prominences. These clouds of gas rising to great heights above the chromosphere are conspicuous to the eye at total eclipses of the Sun. Their rose-pink colour is due to the dominance of Hα in their spectra. Hydrogen, ionized calcium and helium are all conspicuous in prominences. These lines are so bright that it is easy to see and photograph prominences outside eclipse when one uses a spectroscope to isolate the corresponding wavelengths (e.g. with spectrohelioscope, spectroheliograph, etc.). In very bright prominences sodium, magnesium and ionized iron lines can be detected.

At times of solar activity eruptive prominences are commonly shot out to heights of hundreds of thousands of miles in the course of an hour or so. On rare occasions the velocity of rise has exceeded the velocity of escape from the Sun (617 km/sec). However, when cinematograph technique was developed (at speeds of about 2 frames per minute, so that in projection the phenomena are speeded up by a factor about 750 times normal) it was discovered that in apparently quiet prominences fine filaments of matter move predominantly *downwards* into so-called 'centres of attraction', usually near sunspots. The matter tends to follow constant paths in an arched shape. The impression gained from viewing such motion pictures is very strong that the matter is following magnetic lines of force.

Prominences can be seen projected *dark* against the disk on spectroheliograms as well as bright at the limb.

Surges are a particular type of short-lived prominence which on motion pictures appear to shoot out from the Sun and return along the same path. *Flares* consist of intense but short-lived brightenings of hydrogen and other radiations which have assumed practical importance owing to the terrestrial radio fade-outs and magnetic storms which accompany them. Through international co-operation a continuous spectroscopic watch is kept on the Sun for these events.

Curiously enough no marked Doppler shifts have been found (like those in eruptive prominences) in the spectra of flares. But Hα develops very broad wings, probably due to Stark effect and electrical fields.

Corona. The prominences rise into the region occupied by the solar corona. The total light of the corona is only about half that of the full Moon, or one millionth of sunlight. At total eclipses it can be traced faintly out to over 5 solar radii. There is a very strong concentration of light near the Sun, and this inner corona was first detected outside of eclipse by Lyot (1930) after many other astronomers had failed in their attempts to reduce the glare of sunlight.

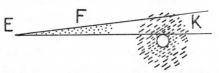

FIG. 26. The polarized *K* corona is due to scattering of light in the true corona near the Sun. The *F* corona (unpolarized) is due to scattering by interplanetary particles between the Earth (*E*) and the Sun.

The spectrum of the corona is continuous with superposed Fraunhofer absorption and a strange bright-line spectrum.

The Fraunhofer lines form a replica of the solar spectrum except that they show less contrast; they are partly filled in by a superposed continuum. The careful measurer of such a spectrum has first to eliminate the effects of skylight scattered from outside the Moon's shadow. The residue is formed of two parts called F and K. F is now attributed to scattering of sunlight by particles between the Earth and the Sun (which produce the *zodiacal light*). K is due to scattering by free electrons in the corona. The corona is known to show considerable polarization, and through the actual physical layout of the situation this must be provided by the K component (close to the Sun) rather than by the F component (see fig. 26).

At one time there was a difficulty in this picture. The K component due to electron scattering was expected to provide a close replica of the Fraunhofer spectrum (like F) without the observed shallowing of the lines. The explanation came after the identification of the coronal emission lines in 1941. These bright lines (never produced in the laboratory) are now known to be due to 'forbidden' radiations by very highly ionized ions, Fe X, Fe XI, Fe XIII, Fe XIV, Ni XVI, etc. (see Appendix V, p. 236). The ionization potentials of the ions concerned range from 233 volts (Fe X) to 814 volts for doubtfully identified Ca XV.

These extremely high ionization potentials pointed to an unexpectedly *hot* corona with a temperature of about a million degrees. At such a temperature the motion of electrons must be so violent that in the light scattered by them the Fraunhofer lines are almost completely blurred out by Doppler effect. The one exception is the strongest feature in the Fraunhofer spectrum, the H and K lines, which do show as a very shallow dip in the spectrum of the corona broadened to about 300 A (as well as the ordinary H and K in the F component). Careful photometry had revealed this dip as early as 1931.

We thus arrive at the following picture of the coronal spectrum: the Fraunhofer spectrum (F component) is due to scattering by interplanetary particles; the continuous (K component) is produced by scattering by electrons moving so fast that they blur out the details of the Fraunhofer spectrum; the bright line spectrum is due to forbidden radiations by heavily ionized atoms of which iron and nickel are the most conspicuous.

The high temperature of the corona also explained a minor puzzle. The emission spectrum shows no Balmer lines of hydrogen and in this respect is almost unique in astrophysics. The reason is that at a million degrees hydrogen is completely ionized into protons and free electrons and the protons have no chance of capturing the fast-moving electrons.

Planetary atmospheres. We have seen that the Sun's spectrum is crossed by absorption lines whose origin lies in the Earth's atmosphere. In fig. 27(*a*) light from the Sun *S* passes once through the Earth's atmosphere before reaching the observer at *O*.

When observing the spectrum of a planet *P*, sunlight passes *twice* through the planet's atmosphere (fig. 27*b*). In the excep-

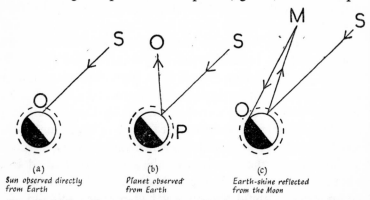

(a)	(b)	(c)
Sun observed directly	Planet observed	Earth-shine reflected
from Earth	from Earth	from the Moon

FIG. 27. (*a*) Sun observed directly from Earth. (*b*) Planet observed from Earth. (*c*) Earth-shine reflected from the Moon. The Sun's rays traverse a planet's atmosphere once (*a*), twice (*b*) and three times (*c*) before reaching the observer *O*.

tional case of the earth-shine on the Moon *M*, the observer from the Earth sees light which has crossed the Earth's atmosphere three times (fig. 27*c*).

The Moon itself has no permanent atmosphere as far as we can tell. Its spectrum is an exact replica of the Sun's. An upper limit of about a millionth of a terrestrial atmosphere can therefore be set. There is probably a thin haze of dust cast up by falling meteors. Sulphur dioxide, which might be formed by meteoritic impact or volcanic action, has been looked for spectroscopically in vain.

In a remarkable observation on November 3, 1958, the Russian astronomer Kozyrev seems to have witnessed an eruption of carbon gas from the crater Alphonsus; bright bands due to C_2 were observed spectroscopically. These bands are familiar in the spectra of comets and were probably excited by solar ultra-violet radiation; however, the CN bands, also very strong in comets, were not found.

Any 'permanent' atmosphere which the Moon possessed must have escaped millions of years ago because its gravity was too feeble to retain it. Atmospheres will be retained longest by heavy cool planets. According to Kuiper the order of decreasing ability within the solar system to retain an atmosphere is: Jupiter, Saturn, Neptune, Uranus, Pluto (?), Earth, Venus, Triton (satellite of Neptune), Mars, Titan (satellite of Saturn), four large satellites of Jupiter, Mercury, Moon, etc.

With the exception of the faint objects Pluto and Triton, atmospheres are known for all these objects from Jupiter to Titan; no atmosphere has been detected for those following Titan.

Jupiter, Saturn, Uranus, Neptune. All four planets are completely cloudbound without any surface features being visible. Secchi and Huggins detected, visually, bands in the spectrum of Uranus. These bands are also present in Jupiter, Saturn and Neptune in increasing strength; it is these bands which give Neptune its strikingly green colour. Slipher detected many more bands in red and infra-red in these major planets.

The origin of these bands remained unknown until 1932 when R. Wildt suggested that they were due to methane and ammonia. Identification with these molecules was clinched soon afterwards by Dunham. The methane bands strengthen markedly from Jupiter to Neptune, while the ammonia bands are weaker in Saturn than in Jupiter. The temperatures of all these planets are very low (of the order of

H

120° K or less) and the ammonia probably tends to be frozen out of the atmospheres of the coldest planets.

It is now realized that H_2 and He are probably the commonest constituents of the atmospheres of these large planets. But no ordinary lines of these substances are likely to be observed through the Earth's atmosphere. However, Herzberg has evidence for four 'forbidden' lines of H_2 in Uranus and Neptune. The brownish colour of Jupiter's belts does not appear to be reflected in any spectroscopic peculiarity and has not been fully explained.

It is interesting that Saturn's rings show a pure solar spectrum as would be expected for a swarm of small particles; however, Kuiper finds some evidence in the far infra-red that the particles are frost-covered or perhaps composed of ice.

Earth. Among the many constituents of the Earth's atmosphere which reveal themselves in the Fraunhofer spectrum, H_2O, O_2 and O_3 are outstanding, the latter being the earthbound astronomer's great obstacle to research at wavelengths shorter than 2975 A. Also known are CO_2, N_2O, CH_4. The commonest known substance N_2 has no suitable bands in the accessible region for spectroscopic detection.

The spectrum of the night sky offers a unique opportunity to study physical processes in a planetary atmosphere. Molecular bands[1] due to OH, O_2, $N_2{}^+$ appear together with the 'forbidden' lines of O I, which appear enormously enhanced in aurorae.

At dawn or sunset the sodium D lines appear strongly in the so-called 'twilight flash'. In the early spectra the pair was unresolved and the identification was clinched in a remarkable manner; a tube containing sodium vapour placed in front of the spectrograph extinguished the emission feature completely; this could not have occurred if the origin of the

[1] The bands all appear in emission; bands therefore appear which cannot be expected to appear in absorption in the Fraunhofer spectrum.

emission lay at a single wavelength intermediate between the two D lines.

Venus. Clouds completely cover this planet and the reason for its very high reflecting power (albedo $= 0.59$) is not understood. High dispersion spectroscopy by Dunham in the infrared revealed new bands due to CO_2 (the original clue to the identification being provided by the separation of lines in the bands, from which the molecular moment of inertia could be derived). Analysis of the band intensities yields a temperature of $300° \pm 50$ K.

Strenuous attempts to detect water vapour and oxygen in the spectrum of Venus have so far failed.[1] The difficulty caused by the fact that terrestrial absorption by these substances is very strong can be partially avoided by observing at times when Venus is approaching or receding from the Earth rapidly, the Doppler shift effecting a separation between the two spectra. It was suggested that formaldehyde ($CH_3.CHO$) might be formed from CO_2 and H_2O by ultraviolet sunlight, but the relevant bands were not found.

Mars. A thin atmosphere must be present around Mars to account for the observed twilight zone. Since conditions on Mars are probably closer to those on Earth than on any other planet of the solar system, the composition of the Martian atmosphere is vital to the problem of the possibility of life outside the Earth.

Just as with Venus, attempts to detect lines due to water vapour and oxygen in the spectrum of Mars have failed. Dunham gives as an upper limit to Martian H_2O and O_2 0.0015 times the terrestrial atmospheric composition. The only evidence for H_2O rests on a difficult infra-red observation by Kuiper which suggests (as for Saturn's rings) that

---

[1] A spectroscope carried to a great height on a balloon in 1959 showed some faint signs of water vapour absorption apparently arising in the atmosphere of Venus.

the Martian polar caps are composed of water-frost. Kuiper has also found similarities in the infra-red reflecting powers of the green areas on Mars with those of terrestrial lichens and mosses, but no firm conclusions can be drawn.

Titan. This large satellite of Saturn shows the presence of methane in its spectrum. It is the only satellite for which we have clear evidence of a permanent atmosphere.

Rotation of planets. The rotations of the atmospheres of Jupiter, Saturn, Uranus and Neptune have all been measured spectroscopically. While Jupiter shows many atmospheric disturbances (especially the Red Spot) and Saturn occasional outbursts which permit direct observation of their periods of rotation, the known periods of rotation for Uranus and Neptune depend largely on the spectroscope.

The rotation of the inner planets is too slow to be measured spectroscopically. But mention should be made of Venus because the period of rotation has not been determined by means of the vague patches in the cloudy atmosphere that are seen only with difficulty. A spectroscopic attempt with high dispersion at Mt Wilson Observatory yielded negative results, from which all we can say is that Venus must rotate with a period longer than two or three weeks.

Comets. For many years our knowledge of the spectra of comets remained meagre. Until recently Halley's comet (1910) was the only bright comet accessible to powerful spectroscopes (concentrated in the northern hemisphere). Comets are at their brightest when nearest to the Sun and consequently can only be observed for short intervals, at low altitudes, often with serious interference from twilight.

The brightest part of a comet is the nucleus surrounded by a coma; when near the Sun tails develop extending to distances of millions of miles. Although sunlight provides the origin of a comet's light, it is not through simple reflection as with a planet. The spectrum of a bright comet consists mainly of bright molecular bands. The Sun's light, particularly in the far ultra-violet, dissociates the molecules and causes them to fluoresce. The sodium D lines appear very strongly in some comets which pass within the Earth's orbit (e.g. Comets 1882 II and Arend-Roland 1957), so strongly that the colour to the eye is distinctly orange. The D lines are excited by resonance, simply absorbing and re-radiating solar light at this wavelength. In the very bright comet of 1882 lines of iron and nickel were observed visually.

The strongest bands in the visible spectrum of comets are due to C_2; other molecules identified include CN, CH, OH, NH, CH^+, NH_2, ? OH^+. A feature near 4050 A, which remained controversial for some time, is probably due to C_3.

When the intensities of individual lines in a band are measured it is possible to derive a 'rotational temperature' for the particular molecule. The values found for CN are about 300 to 400° K; the temperature tends to increase for smaller distances from the Sun, as expected. However, such analyses are complicated by the fact that instead of a regular progression of intensities along the band, some lines are remarkably weak. P. Swings explained this beautifully by showing that the weak lines corresponded in wavelength to strong Fraunhofer lines in the Sun's spectrum (after allowance for Doppler shifts). This meant that the molecular band in question must be excited by *resonance*; the intensity of each line in the band being dependent on how much solar radiation is available to excite it.

The tails of comets show strong bands due to CO^+, N_2^+ and also CH^+ and CO_2^+. It is interesting that these are all ionized molecules, doubtless due to the continued dissociating influence of sunlight on gases which have escaped for some time from the nucleus. The dissociating energy may be provided not only by the ultra-violet sunlight but also by particles shot out from the Sun (such as those which produce aurorae). One comet (Schwassmann-Wachmann) is subject to abrupt increases in light, which may be connected with outbursts on the Sun.

Meteors. The spectra of meteors are difficult to observe, but with the development of fast Schmidt cameras the number of good meteor spectra obtained has increased markedly in recent years. Emission lines due to neutral Na, Fe, Ca, Mn, Cr, Si, Ni and Al have been found. Ionized lines of Ca, Fe, Mg, Si are also observed in rapid meteors; Ca II H and K dominate the spectra of Perseids (60 km/sec), but no ionized lines are found when the speed is less than 30 km/sec. The energy of ionization is readily understood as supplied by the speed of impact with the Earth's atmosphere. Traces of many other elements can of course be detected spectroscopically in meteorites which are recovered on the Earth's surface.

Chapter 8

DOUBLE STARS

Direct telescopic inspection of the stars nearest the Sun shows that at least one star in five is double. The spectroscope shows that duplicity is no rarer a phenomenon among the luminous early-type stars which are too far away to be resolved as visual doubles.

We have known ever since William Herschel's time that the orbital motions of visual double stars are governed by the same Newtonian laws that control the planets in the solar system. Through the study of double stars we have our only direct means of measuring stellar *masses*, since Newtonian mechanics directly connects the period of orbital motion, the size of the orbit and the masses of the components of a double star.[1]

In the case of spectroscopic binaries we find that the radial velocities, of one or two stars, vary with time but repeat themselves regularly after a certain period, which may be anything from a few hours to 100 days or more. We cannot observe most spectroscopic binaries continuously through one period; but on the assumption of regular

---

[1] $M_1 + M_2 = A^3/P^2$ where M_1, M_2 are the masses of the two stars (Sun's mass = 1), A = semi-major-axis of the orbit in astronomical units, P = period in years. Kepler's third law A^3/P^2 = constant applies to the planets in the solar system because here the mass of every planet (M_2) is negligibly small compared with the Sun's (M_1). For double stars, observations of the relative motion yields only the combined mass; we can derive M_1, M_2 separately if the motion of each star relative to an external frame of reference (meridian circle) is measured.

repetition we assemble all the observations of radial velocity, which may be scattered over several years, on the period that best satisfies all the observations and so derive a radial velocity curve. Such curves turn out to be exactly what one would expect for stars moving in elliptical orbits according to Newtonian mechanics.

Suppose we have a spectroscopic binary showing two spectra and that we have deduced the period of the system. In the simplest case of pure circular motions about the centre of gravity, the radial velocity curves for both stars A and B

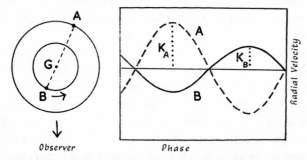

Fig. 28. Radial velocity curves for a spectroscopic binary with circular orbits. B has twice the mass of A. The horizontal line on the right corresponds to the radial velocity of G, the centre of gravity of the system.

will be simple sine-waves (fig. 28). We can draw a horizontal line cutting both curves such that the areas above and below the line are the same. This line defines the radial velocity of the centre of gravity G of the system.

The semi-amplitudes K_A, K_B of the two curves need not be the same. In the case drawn, B is clearly the heavier star with a smaller orbit. We can deduce the *ratio of the masses* immediately from the observed ranges in velocity of the two stars.[1]

In the case drawn we have supposed the observer to be in

[1] $M_A/M_B = K_B/K_A.$

the plane of the orbit. In general of course this is not so; and then the amplitudes of the variations in velocity will be reduced, but *in the same ratio*.[1]

Despite this doubt about the orientation of the orbit we can still derive the ratio of the masses directly from the ratio K_A/K_B. The nearest we can come to measuring individual masses from the radial velocities is to determine $M_A \sin^3 i$, and $M_B \sin^3 i$. In general there is unfortunately no means of measuring the inclination i separately.

When only one spectrum can be observed in a spectroscopic binary, still less information can of course be extracted from the observed radial velocities. Nevertheless such observations are of value statistically in problems of stellar masses.

When the orbits are elliptical instead of circular we find radial velocity curves of the shapes sketched on the right of fig. 29. The star moves most rapidly when nearest the centre of gravity G, near the arrows shown on the left of the diagram. The corresponding portions of the radial velocity curves are shown by straight arrows on the right. The short time spent by the star near G accounts for the rapid change from negative to positive velocities in the upper diagram, when the major axis of the orbit is pointed towards the observer; similarly, in the lower diagram, with the major axis at right angles to the line of sight, the star spends a short time passing through the sharp peak of negative velocity (approach).

Eclipsing binaries. Many spectroscopic binaries are also eclipsing binaries (like Algol) in which one star periodically passes in front of and totally or partially eclipses the other. In most cases the variations in light and velocity are entirely consistent with one another: the periods are the same, and eclipses take place when the radial velocity is near its average

[1] The factor of reduction is sin i, where i is the inclination of the orbit to the plane of the sky.

value, just as we would expect. The great importance of eclipsing binaries is that we know that the inclination i must be nearly 90°; the actual value of i can be derived from precise light-curves. It is therefore possible to deduce individual masses of spectroscopic binaries showing two spectra which are also eclipsing binaries.

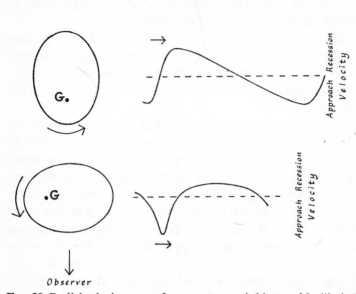

FIG. 29. Radial velocity curves for a spectroscopic binary with elliptical orbits.

Mass–luminosity relation. When stellar masses became known for a sufficient number of visual and spectroscopic binaries, whose *distances* were also known, it became clear that there was a fairly close relationship between a star's mass and its luminosity. Stars of about one-fifth the Sun's mass have only 2 per cent of the Sun's luminosity, while at the other end of the scale stars of about 30 solar masses radiate 100,000 times as much as the Sun.

This mass–luminosity relation was first explained theoretically by Eddington in 1924 on the basis of his studies of the structure of stellar interiors; Eddington's result was all the more remarkable in that it was achieved without knowledge of the way in which stellar energy was generated.

The fairly small scatter about the mean in the observed mass–luminosity relation is a direct indication that the average composition of stars is by and large the same.[1] However, white dwarfs do have luminosities far less than those for ordinary stars of the same mass; this is because the white dwarfs have a totally different structure. There are some apparently well-established cases of stars that are too bright for their masses and which show no other very marked peculiarities. This could arise if the stars in question had less hydrogen in their interiors than normal. This problem cannot be pursued further here, but it hardly needs stressing that accurate spectroscopic observations of any stars showing such deviations from the mass–luminosity relation are of pressing importance.

Early-type binaries. In addition to information about masses, spectroscopic observations of binaries, especially those of early type, have taught us much about individual stars that we could not have learnt otherwise.

Among the binaries of types O, B or A we find that periods of 1 to 20 days predominate. Owing to the great distances of O and B stars orbital motions among them are only detected spectroscopically. It is obvious that spectroscopic binaries with large ranges in velocity are the most easily detected. Large stellar masses or large eccentricity in the orbit are associated with large velocities, so that observational discovery favours systems with these properties.

[1] This depends on the theoretical result that the predicted luminosity depends on the fourth power of the mean molecular weight of stellar material. See p. 210, footnote.

Most early-type binaries have shallow diffuse lines, and this has been attributed to rapid *axial rotation* of the stars (Chap. 14, p. 204). It is possible to estimate the speed of rotation from the widths of the lines. But a much more direct approach is possible in the case of an eclipsing binary.

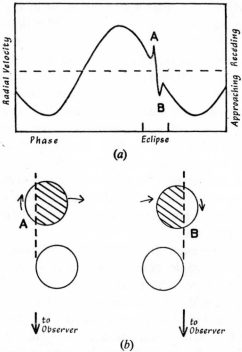

FIG. 30. (*a*) Rotation effect in an eclipsing binary. The sine-wave variation in radial velocity is distorted during eclipse. (*b*) The eclipse of a rotating star. Just before mid-eclipse only the receding edge of the eclipsed star is visible. After eclipse, the approaching edge is seen first.

Fig. 30*a* shows the radial velocity curve of the brighter component of an eclipsing binary, in which a complicated kink *AB* is observed at the time of eclipse. Before total eclipse the lines show an excess shift to the red; immediately after they show an excess shift to the violet.

The explanation is simple. At phase *A*, illustrated in fig. 30*b*, the brighter component (which has of course been receding from us before it is eclipsed) is beginning to be eclipsed. The excess velocity of recession means that the remaining crescent is spinning away from us; as the opposite crescent emerges from eclipse (phase *B*) we find that it is spinning towards us. The sense of rotation is always in the same sense as the orbital motion.

The speeds of rotation that are measured in this way cannot of course compare in accuracy with similar measures of the Sun's rotation where the slit of the spectroscope isolates light from the opposite limbs. But the velocities measured in early-type stars are large, reaching values up to several hundred km/sec.

Combination of spectroscopic data with the light-curve of an eclipsing binary enables us to measure the diameters of the two stars in kilometres. If then we have also derived the stellar speeds of rotation, we can compute the rotational *periods*. It is interesting that the periods so found very often agree precisely with the orbital period; the two stars keep the same face turned to each other, doubtless through tidal action just as the Moon always turns the same face to the Earth. This is the general rule for spectroscopic binaries with periods of three days or less. Exceptions are frequent for longer orbital periods where the rotations appear to be too fast.

W Ursae Majoris. This eclipsing binary is characteristic of a group (the W Ursa Majoris or UMa group) which has attracted much attention in recent years. It consists of two nearly equal dwarf F8 stars which eclipse each other every 4 hours, the total period being 8 hours. A great many such binaries have been discovered by their light-variation and Shapley estimates that they outnumber all other variable stars put together. Many more early-type binaries are known, but Shapley's conclusion is based on calculations of frequency *in space*. The W UMa stars are not so easily detected as the more luminous early-type binaries for exactly the same reason that makes the discovery of all dwarfs more difficult than that of giants (p. 65).

Since the W UMa stars tend to be faint, few have been observed spectroscopically, but Struve finds that the two dwarf stars are nearly in contact, that the masses are usually close to that of the Sun, and that the spectra are restricted to the range G0 to K0. Perhaps the most remarkable spectroscopic result, still not fully explained, is that when the lines are seen double *the violet component is almost invariably stronger than the red component*, no matter which star is approaching us at the time. Struve has suggested that gas envelopes the whole system and that this envelope is deeper on the forward side of each star.

Many eclipsing binaries show features in their spectra of absorbing individual interest. We now proceed to consider a few of the most important of such individual stars.

RW Tauri. This binary consists of a K0 giant and a smaller B9 star. During total eclipse the K spectrum alone remains, but for a short time before and after totality, bright hydrogen lines are observed; before totality the hydrogen emission is displaced some 340 km/sec to the red, while on emergence from eclipse the emission is displaced similarly to the violet. This sequence of events was discovered by Joy with the Mt Wilson 100-inch telescope; it was a difficult observation because the star is rather faint and totality lasts only 80 minutes.

The explanation is shown diagrammatically in fig. 31. The hydrogen emission is attributed to a rapidly rotating ring of gas around the B9 star. Outside eclipse, the emission ring is invisible in the spectrum against the glare of the central star. But when the B star has been eclipsed, the receding part of the ring (*R*) is still visible round the edge of the K star. The first sign of emergence from eclipse is the other side of the ring, V (approaching with velocity 340 km/sec).

The intensities of red and violet components vary from one eclipse to another in such a way as to suggest that there are real variations in the ring with time.

Some 15 stars in all are known to possess gaseous rings like RW Tau. In all cases the order of events is the same. This means that the direction of rotation of the ring is the same as that of the orbital motion.

Absorbing shells. As a corollary to the bright gaseous rings like that around RW Tau, some stars seem to be surrounded

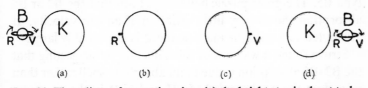

FIG. 31. The eclipse of a rotating ring. (*a*) the bright star is about to be eclipsed by the K giant. No emission lines can be seen in the spectrum. (*b*) the B star is eclipsed, but emission lines (shifted to the red) are seen, due to the receding side of the ring. (*c*) Just before the B star emerges, emission lines (shifted to the violet) are seen, due to the approaching side of the ring.

by shells of gas which reveal themselves by sharp lines superposed on a diffuse spectrum. This is not regarded as a double star because no orbital motion can be detected. The central star shows a diffuse spectrum because of rapid rotation. The shell may have been thrown out by centrifugal force. But at a certain distance from the central star, the shell seems to persist in a quiescent state with sharp lines.

The star Pleione in the Pleiades developed such a shell temporarily in 1938 but this has gradually changed since. One of the features of the shell spectrum is the great weakness of lines of Mg II and Si II. These particular lines arise from energy levels from which strong downward transitions are possible. This means that while they are absorbed strongly in an ordinary stellar atmosphere, the lines will be weak if formed at a great distance from a star's surface (where the radiation is diluted to feeble intensity). Struve calculated that the weakening of these lines in Pleione indicated a ring with a radius two or three times that of the central star.

β Lyrae. This famous naked-eye star was one of the earliest eclipsing binaries discovered. Its spectrum is extremely complicated, consisting of a B9 star whose velocity changes by 367 km/sec in a period of 12·9 days. There is also an absorption spectrum of type B2 or B5, and an emission spectrum of type B5. The great puzzle has always been that the B2 or B5 absorption shows very little variation, if any, in velocity. If attributed to a star, the mass deduced is improbably large.

Struve found a way out of this difficulty by suggesting that the B2–B5 absorption is due to an absorbing shell rather than to a star; the weakness of Mg II and Si II in the spectrum parallels that found in the shell around Pleione. There must be a second star present to account for the orbital motion of the B9 star, and in Struve and Kuiper's model they propose that it is an invisible F star which shares an atmosphere with the B9 star. Gaseous streams pass from one to the other, some passing outwards to escape altogether from the system.[1]

ζ Aurigae. A much simpler, and extremely informative, eclipsing system is that of *ζ* Aurigae. This consists of a K type supergiant and a relatively small B star. Every 972 days

[1] Struve and his colleagues have found evidence of streams of gas passing between members of a number of other spectroscopic binaries. Absorption lines due to such streams distort the radial velocity curves. This discovery constitutes a warning against automatically interpreting the radial velocities literally as representing motions of two stars. The danger signal is seen if there is a discrepancy between analyses of the radial velocities and of the *light-curves* of an eclipsing variable. This often occurs when the two components are relatively close to one another. (See O. Struve and Shu Shu Huang, *Occ. Notes, R.A.S.*, No. 9, 1957.)

the K star eclipses the B star which remains invisible for about 60 days. The critical phases when the B star is passing into and out of eclipse last only about one day. During these phases new strong absorption lines appear in the spectrum, which are reminiscent of the Sun's chromospheric spectrum; the lines of Ca II, Ti II and other ionized metals are prominent.

From the changes in light it is deduced that the radius of the B star is only 1/56 that of the K supergiant. During partial eclipse therefore the B star acts as a point source

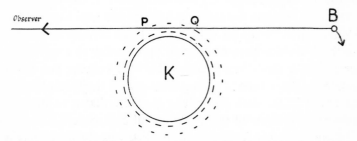

Fig. 32. Zeta Aurigae. The small B star is passing behind the atmosphere of the K supergiant. Lines appear temporarily in the spectrum, due to absorption by atoms in the section PQ of the K atmosphere.

behind different portions of the extended atmosphere of the K star (fig. 32). We can measure the rate of growth of intensity of the chromospheric lines as the B star sinks into eclipse;[1] these measures can be directly related to the density of atoms at various heights above the photosphere of the K star. We can thus analyse the structure of the chromosphere of a supergiant in much the same way as we analyse the solar chromosphere by watching the disappearance or reappearance of 'flash' lines at a total solar eclipse.

[1] The B star is strong in violet and ultra-violet light (where the K star is weak) and it is only in this part of the spectrum that the new chromospheric lines can be detected.

One of the extraordinary features of the ζ Aurigae system is that the phenomena do not repeat themselves exactly from eclipse to eclipse. Sometimes the atmosphere of the K star extends to much greater heights than usual. It looks as if on these occasions the K star is swollen by vast eruptions of gases, perhaps similar to the solar prominences on a grand scale. Supergiants are known to be subject to irregular variations in apparent radial velocity or in light. With such an enormous output of energy they may be near the verge of instability, and local variations within the atmosphere are not altogether surprising.

Several systems similar to ζ Aurigae are now known, for example o^1 Cygni and VV Cephei. Each favourable eclipse of these systems presents a great opportunity to analyse the details of a star's atmosphere. Since the eclipses last for a relatively short time in a long total period they are not easy to detect in the first place. It is probable that a number of important systems of this type are still undiscovered.

Symbiotic stars. This picturesque title was given by Merrill to certain peculiar objects which combine characteristics of the hottest and coolest ends of the spectral sequence. A nebular spectrum with bright lines of ionized helium is found in conjunction with an M-type absorption characterized by Ti O bands. All such stars are variable in the light which they emit, and are sometimes subject to an outburst like a nova. It is not known for certain whether two separate stars are always involved, although this is the case with Antares and Mira Ceti, and in two cases (VV Cephei and AR Pavonis) an eclipse is observed to occur. Very probably two 'nuclei' are involved in a single nebula. The symbiotic stars might represent a transient phase in the birth of a double star.

Chapter 9

GASEOUS NEBULAE

Types of nebulae. The word *nebula* (literally a *little cloud*) was introduced by early astronomers to describe many objects which appeared in their small telescopes as fuzzy patches reminiscent of small terrestrial clouds seen faintly illuminated.

It needed only slightly more powerful telescopes to show that some of the original 'nebulae' could be resolved into compact clusters of faint stars. The white *spiral nebulae,* avoiding the plane of the Milky Way, required the 100-inch telescope to resolve the brightest stars and these systems are now better termed *galaxies.*

Among the remaining nebulae, Sir William Herschel recognized *planetary nebulae* (with roundish shapes resembling a planet) as distinct from the more irregular *diffuse nebulae,* of which the Orion nebula is the best known. He correctly guessed that no telescope, however powerful, would resolve these nebulae into separate stars. Some astronomers preferred to believe that *all* nebulae consisted of stars, and that lack of resolution was only due to the limited power of their telescopes.

Gaseous nature of nebulae. It was the spectroscope that gave the conclusive answer to this problem. Observers had noted a greenish tinge in the planetaries and to a less extent in the diffuse nebulae. When Huggins turned his spectroscope at a planetary in the constellation of Draco in 1864 he was astonished to see this green light concentrated in one bright line, with no trace of continuous spectrum. In Huggins' own words he could immediately conclude 'Not an aggregation of stars, but a luminous gas'. Later Huggins was able to establish, also spectroscopically, the gaseous nature of such diffuse nebulae as that in Orion.

Here was immediate proof of enormous tracts of space (vastly exceeding the solar system in size) filled with luminous gas. It was perhaps the most momentous discovery in astronomy since Galileo turned his telescope to the skies. Many discoveries in the field of astronomical spectroscopy can still be made in an instant of time, like Huggins', through the examination under an eyepiece of a spectrum on a plate still wet from the photographic processing.

The puzzle of nebulium. The green line first seen by Huggins had no counterpart in the laboratory spectrum of any known terrestrial substance; to this day it has not been observed in a laboratory source. This is also true of a fainter line found later by Huggins. A third neighbouring line could be identified with $H\beta$.

Huggins attributed the two unidentified lines to an unknown element which he called *nebulium*. However, as time passed it was realized that the Periodic Table of elements left no room for an atom likely to be identified with nebulium. Improvements in laboratory techniques brought out some spectra of familiar atoms that had remained unidentified in the stars. The impression grew that nebulium might prove to be a familiar element shining in unfamiliar conditions.

It was not till 1927, during the extremely active era of analysis of atomic energy levels that Bowen brilliantly succeeded in proving that nebulium was in fact oxygen; the green lines are radiated by doubly ionized oxygen and the almost perfect vacuum of interstellar space favours this radiation over the more familiar lines of this ion found in the laboratory.

The Grotrian diagram of the lowest levels of O III is shown in fig. 33. There are numerous higher levels, but for simplicity only one triplet level (designated ^{3}X) and one singlet level (^{1}Y) appear on the diagram. Transitions between ^{1}S, ^{1}D and ^{3}P are forbidden by the selection rules so that no corresponding lines are observed in the laboratory; all three levels are metastable (p. 49). However, Bowen advanced convincing arguments for believing that the transitions between ^{1}D and two of the ^{3}P states would produce lines with the observed wavelengths of the two nebulium lines. The transition ^{1}S–^{1}D also corresponds to the wavelength 4363 A, another line found in the nebulae.

The proof lay partly in simple arithmetic and partly in following the detailed behaviour of the various 'forbidden' lines in various nebulae. Whenever there is a state (such as ^{1}Y) which combines with two lower states (^{1}S and ^{1}D) to give two observed laboratory lines, it is possible to calculate directly the difference in energy between those states and hence to predict the wavelength of the forbidden transition ^{1}S–^{1}D.[1] The agreement of the observed wavelength (4363 A) with that predicted furnishes direct evidence that this particular nebular line is to be identified with [O III].[2]

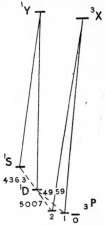

FIG. 33. Grotrian diagram of O III (lowest states). Dashed transitions are 'forbidden'. The wavelength (4363) of the transition ^{1}S–^{1}D is predicted from laboratory observations of lines connected with ^{1}Y. The difference in wavelength (48 A) of the two transitions ^{1}D–^{3}P$_{2,1}$ is predicted from laboratory observations of lines connected with ^{3}X.

[1] As already mentioned (p. 104) the solar spectrum shows numerous examples of *permitted* lines due to Fe etc. which have not been produced in the laboratory, but whose identification is certain because of agreement with predicted wavelengths and of considerations of intensities.

[2] Square brackets are used around the symbol of an element to indicate a forbidden transition.

No such direct proof is possible in the case of the two green 'nebulium' lines. No energy level of O III combines with both ^{1}D and ^{3}P to give permitted lines observed in the laboratory. But observed transitions like ^{3}X–^{3}P$_2$ and ^{3}X–^{3}P$_1$ fix the energy difference between ^{3}P$_2$ and ^{3}P$_1$; this enables us to say that *if* the unknown energy difference between ^{1}D and ^{3}P is such as to put the forbidden lines connecting them near 5000 A in the green, then the separation of the two lines must be about 48 A; this is in fact the separation of the two

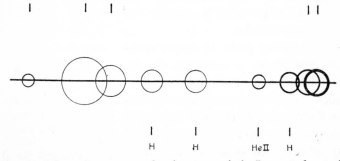

Fig. 34. Schematic spectrum of a planetary nebula. In most planetaries the monochromatic images show considerable irregularities, and the diagram exaggerates the differences in size between the various images. Identifications of forbidden lines appear above, of permitted lines below.

nebulium lines. Thus the identification of these two lines with [O III] rests, in the first place, on a rather arbitrary placing of the ^{1}D level in the Grotrian diagram.

Here another type of spectroscopic observation comes to our aid with useful supplementary information. With a slitless spectroscope a typical planetary nebula presents an appearance as sketched in fig. 34. A faint central star is usually found – spread out in the spectrum into the horizontal line of the figure. The nebula itself appears as a series of monochromatic images at various wavelengths. These images vary in size.

Ionized helium (4686) gives a very small image; neutral helium and the nebulium lines appear larger. The largest images appear in the ultra-violet at 3727 A. It is found that the size depends closely on the ionization potential; ions with the highest ionization potential are concentrated towards the centre of the nebula. The two nebulium lines always show monochromatic images of the same size – and roughly the same size as the line 4363. This gives us confidence in ascribing all three lines to [O III].

A further clue comes from the relative intensities of lines in various nebulae. For the two nebulium lines 5007 is always found to be about three times as strong as 4959, while their intensities relative to other lines vary. In the planetaries and the diffuse nebulae 4363 is always considerably weaker than the green nebulium lines, but may be of comparable strength in some other objects. This is now explained in terms of different conditions of density and temperature.

In the accompanying table are listed some of the most important forbidden lines commonly observed in planetary nebulae. It is to be noted that the extensive astrophysical observations and reasoning (combined with the laboratory observations) which have served to identify these lines, have also served to fix atomic energy levels (like that of ^1D in fig. 33). Such knowledge could not have been won on the basis of laboratory observations alone.[1]

The production of forbidden lines. How does it happen that these forbidden lines appear in nebulae and not in the laboratory?

In brief, the forbidden lines *are* emitted by atoms in the

---

[1] The green auroral line at 5577 A identified with [O I] in the laboratory by McLennan is an exception; the successful production of this forbidden line of a neutral atom provides a welcome confirmation of the astrophysical reasoning leading to the identification of forbidden lines of more heavily ionized atoms.

REPRESENTATIVE FORBIDDEN LINES
IN PLANETARY NEBULAE

Wavelength	Ion	Wavelength	Ion
3345	Ne V	5007	O III
3425	Ne V	5755	N II
3726	O III	6300	O I
3729	O III	6312	S III
3868	Ne III	6363	O I
3967	Ne III	6548	N II
4068	S II	6584	N II
4363	O III	7320	O II
4740	Ar IV	7330	O II
4959	O III	7751	Ar III

laboratory but so faintly that they are not observed. They are emitted as faintly in a planetary nebula but the depth of the nebula is so enormous that the intensity of the faint glow builds up to the point of visibility.

By contrast, the permitted lines, so familiar in the laboratory, are much more difficult to produce in the ultra-vacuum that exists in a nebula and tend to be suppressed relative to the forbidden lines.

In a discharge tube emitting the spectrum of O III, the ions and electrons are frequently colliding with each other or with the walls with energies of 40 electron-volts or more. This is enough to excite the ions to upper states such as ^3X and ^1Y; they can only stay there for a 100 millionth of a second and then emit a permitted line. An atom in a metastable state such as ^1S or ^1D must remain there for about 1 second before it is likely to make a downward transition emitting a forbidden line. No atom in a discharge tube can expect to be left in peace so long as that.

In a typical planetary nebula the density is so low that there are only about 10^3 to 10^4 ions per cm^3. Collisions are so rare that ions have plenty of time to make the downward forbidden transitions. But low density is not the only condition required.

There must not be too much ultra-violet radiation. If an O III ion in the ^{1}D state should absorb a quantum raising it to state ^{1}Y this would offer a means of escape from the metastable state without emitting the nebulium lines. If the radiation is sufficiently intense, it will prefer this alternative route.

Now the central stars of planetary nebulae are very hot stars, rich in ultra-violet radiation. However, the radiation is weakened in two important ways before it reaches the outer parts of the nebula. First there is the factor of distance; the intensity falls off with the inverse square of the distance from the central star. Secondly, and still more important, the beam of radiation is absorbed heavily in the process of ionizing atoms and ions on its way out. This is why the ions with highest ionization potential are found concentrated towards the central star with the smallest monochromatic images.

The puzzle of nebulium is completely solved by the combination of the results of spectrum analysis, the observation of varying sizes of monochromatic images, and the physical reasoning that conditions in the planetary nebulae are favourable to the production of forbidden lines.

Permitted lines in planetary nebulae. Besides the forbidden lines, the spectra of nebulae contain strong lines of hydrogen, helium, oxygen and a few other light elements. At the head of the Balmer series of hydrogen there is a continuous spectrum (just as in the solar chromosphere; p. 43) which is due to the capture of free electrons by ionized hydrogen. A faint continuum whose interpretation is still a matter of discussion also appears at other wavelengths.

Permitted lines of O III and N III show peculiar intensities compared with the laboratory, and the identifications might be doubted but for another piece of brilliant interpretation by Bowen. The lines of O III which are peculiarly enhanced are connected either directly or very closely with one particular energy level; the anomaly can be explained by any mechanism which would selectively excite O III ions into that level. Bowen noticed that the level is connected with the ground state by the resonance line at 303·799 A, very close to the He II resonance line 303·780 A. We expect the latter line to be a very strong emission line in the nebulae (it is much too far in the ultra-violet to be observed). Thus He II emission would provide a very efficient mechanism for selectively exciting O III ions and producing the observed permitted radiation. Variations from nebula to nebula may be expected, and do occur, since Doppler shifts of the He II and O III lines will strongly affect the efficiency of the mechanism.

By an extraordinary chance, the cycle of O III transitions is ended by a line at 374·436 A which coincides closely with two resonance lines of N III (374·434 and 374·442 A). Thus another cycle of selectively excited N III lines is set up, again in agreement with observation.

Temperatures of planetary nuclei. The hot star usually found at the centre of a planetary nebula is the source of all the energy which makes the nebula visible. The spectra of these planetary nuclei are of the rare Wolf-Rayet type and they include the hottest stars known with temperatures up to about 100,000° K. It is through the spectra of planetary nebulae that these high temperatures have been measured.

A hot star like this radiates mostly in the extreme ultra-violet as shown by the continuous curve in fig. 35a. Most of this radiation is of shorter wavelength than 912 A (the Lyman limit) and can therefore ionize the hydrogen gas in the surrounding nebula. A hydrogen atom that has lost its electron will eventually capture another in one of the high levels and cascade back to the ground level emitting a quantum at each jump. This process of ionization from the ground level is represented by the upward arrow on the left of fig. 35b (which shows the familiar Grotrian diagram of hydrogen); the

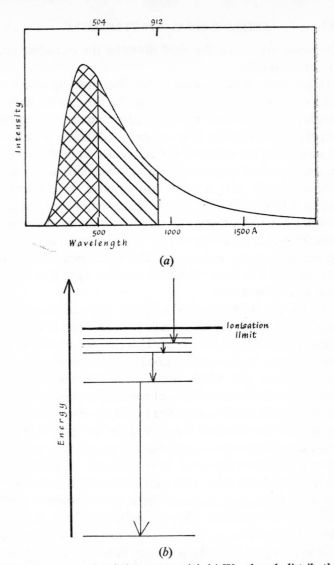

FIG. 35. Temperatures of planetary nuclei. (*a*) Wavelength distribution of radiation from a star at temperature 70,000° K. All the radiation to the left of 912 A can ionize hydrogen, all to the left of 504 A can ionize helium. (*b*) Transformation of quanta beyond 912 A into lower-energy quanta in a planetary nebula.

downward arrows on the right illustrate the cascading process of recapture.

It is a reasonable approximation that every quantum of radiation beyond 912 A (represented by the hatched area in fig. 35a) is absorbed and transformed eventually into a quantum of the Balmer series of hydrogen plus Balmer continuum.[1] By measuring the observed Balmer radiation in the nebula, we can obtain a measure of the unobservable ultra-violet radiation *of the star*. We can also measure the continuous radiation from the star in the visible region of the spectrum. Planck's law tells us how the ratio of visible to ultra-violet radiation varies with temperature. In this way Zanstra found the temperatures of planetary nuclei to be about 50,000° K. The method has been refined in various ways but always leads to similar results.

As we saw from Huggins' original observation, most of the visible radiation from the nebula takes place in the form of the forbidden nebulium lines. This energy comes from the free electrons in the nebula. Look at the upward arrow in fig. 35b. That part which stretches beyond the ionization limit (the heavy horizontal line) represents energy given to the electron in escaping from the hydrogen atom. The hotter the central star the more energy will go into these free electrons. One might expect this gas of free electrons to be as hot as the central star. However, these electrons will collide with O III ions (or any other ions with similar metastable states) and in so doing give up their kinetic energy which is transformed into radiation like the nebulium lines. Oxygen, nitrogen and neon all have suitable metastable states and their ions help to keep the planetary nebulae relatively cool. The forbidden lines can be regarded as 'heat rays' of far longer wavelength than that of the original radiation from the

---

[1] This depends on hydrogen exceeding all other elements in abundance as is now generally held, see p. 210.

nucleus. As compared with the very high temperatures of the central stars, the temperatures of the planetary nebulae themselves are about 10,000° K.

Temperatures and densities of nebulae. Temperatures (measured according to the velocities of electrons) and densities within nebulae can be derived theoretically from the relative intensities of certain forbidden lines (for example [O III] (4959 + 5007)/4363). Conditions in the nebulae are far from those of thermodynamic equilibrium, which is a fair approximation in a star's atmosphere; instead the basic assumption is that the number of atoms or ions entering any particular energy level is equal to the number leaving that level per second. The task of the theorist is to compute the chances of these events through collisions or radiative processes.

Observationally we require accurate measures of the intensities of the appropriate forbidden lines; often these are widely separated by 2000 A or more. When this happens the observations themselves become more difficult, and further they must be corrected for reddening by interstellar matter. A very useful indicator of density is the close pair [O II] 3726, 3729 whose relative intensity can be easily measured without requiring correction.

Diffuse nebulae. The same arguments can be used to determine temperatures and densities within diffuse nebulae, whose spectra are not dissimilar to those of the planetaries. Diffuse nebulae rarely have a single source of excitation like the planetaries; their radiation is excited by clusters of early type B and O stars. With a patchy distribution of these hot stars it is not surprising that we find conditions of temperature and density varying from point to point.

A particularly remarkable feature of some diffuse nebulae that is receiving much attention is the bright boundary that often appears around a dark cloud embedded in a bright diffuse nebula. In general appearance like the silver lining to terrestrial clouds, they are certainly not due to starlight from behind the dark cloud. A characteristic shape of the dark clouds has led to their being called 'elephant trunks'; the trunks usually point towards a hot exciting star, and the bright rim tends to be brightest on the side nearest to the star.

Expansion of planetary nebulae. When the spectra of planetary nebulae are examined with high-dispersion the lines are often found to be split in two, the separation being greatest near the centre of the nebula. These bowed shapes were at first erroneously attributed to rotation. They are now much more reasonably understood in terms of expansion of the gases.

Lines of low excitation and ionization potential tend to show the largest splitting. These are just the lines which show the largest monochromatic images, i.e. which originate furthest from the central star. In the model of expanding gases, we imagine that the heavily ionized atoms concentrated to the centre are given a small outward velocity (more or less the same in all directions). As one proceeds outwards, two things happen: the expansion velocity increases steadily, and the gas becomes less ionized. Both these tendencies can be understood in terms of an intense source of ultra-violet radiation provided by the central star. The surrounding gases absorb this radiation, pick up momentum and are forced outwards. Further out, the ions are exposed to less intense radiation and can capture electrons, but they are nevertheless still accelerated away from the central star, thus giving rise to the widest splitting for the least ionized atoms.

Motions in diffuse nebulae. Slit spectra first showed that various portions of the Orion nebula had different radial velocities with a range of some 10 km/sec. Spectroscopy of individual portions of a nebula is time-consuming. A far more economical method is by means of an interferometer using monochromatic radiation from the nebula. In this way the whole nebula can be studied in one photograph. The different velocities show up in a twisting of the ring-patterns given by the interferometer.

However, in a highly condensed object like a planetary, a set of closely spaced slits will give a series of line-images of parallel sections of the nebula, for each of which radial velocities can be measured.

H II regions. The conspicuous diffuse nebulae are all found close to the plane of the Milky Way. The introduction of fast nebular spectrographs showed that there were much wider tracts of the Milky Way emitting hydrogen radiation feebly. The emission is once again due to the presence of hot stars, as in the brighter diffuse nebulae, and to the capture of free electrons by ionized hydrogen. Such regions, in which the hydrogen is mostly ionized, are called H II regions; those outside where it is mostly neutral are H I regions. Within the largest H II regions one can often identify an individual O star or group of O stars responsible for the ionization. Strömgren calculated the distance from single stars at different temperatures within which the hydrogen would be ionized, on the simplifying assumption that the density of interstellar hydrogen was strictly constant. If the constant density is taken as 10^{-23} gm/cm^3, the H II regions are spheres whose radii increase rapidly from 0·5 parsecs for central A0 stars, to 26 parsecs for B0 stars and as much as 140 parsecs for O6 stars.[1]

The observations of H II regions pervading such great distances within the Milky Way leads on to the subject of what other constituents, besides hydrogen, can be found spectroscopically or otherwise between the stars.

[1] The radii of these 'Strömgren spheres' varies as $N^{-2/3}$ where N is the number of H particles per cm^3.

Chapter 10

INTERSTELLAR MATTER

The whole of observational astrophysics depends upon the remarkable transparency of interstellar space. The view that space was perfectly transparent except for localized regions like the Orion nebula, the southern Coalsack or the dark irregular 'holes' in the Milky Way which appear on photographs, was widely held until 1930.

Yet we now know that interstellar space contains a thin general stratum of gas and particles. In the Milky Way plane the density of the gas is roughly one hydrogen atom per cm^3, and to every thousand hydrogen atoms we may expect to find very roughly one solid particle.[1] The volume of interstellar space is so vast that near the Sun the total mass of gas and particles between the stars is probably not very different from the total mass of stars.

Interstellar gas. The interstellar hydrogen and other light gases reveal themselves in *emission* in the diffuse nebulae and the fainter H II regions described in the last Chapter.

In 1904 Hartmann discovered sharp absorption lines of Ca II (H and K) in the spectroscopic binary δ Orionis. The Ca II lines did not share the orbital motion of the binary but showed a small constant velocity relative to the Sun. One possible explanation was that this absorption arose close to the star in a circumstellar cloud. Many astronomers however believed that it originated in interstellar space. This conclu-

---

[1] Radio astronomers find that the density of interstellar hydrogen is apparently *less* towards the centre of the Milky Way than near the Sun.

sion received support from the observation of similarly sharp but strong H and K lines in the spectra of new stars.

The strongest support came from radial velocities of the calcium lines in early B type stars. In Chapter 6 we saw how these stars exhibit the effects of galactic rotation in their radial velocities. It was found that the sharp H and K lines gave radial velocities varying with galactic longitude just like the stars (fig. 23) but with *half the amplitude*. It will be remembered that the amplitude of the variation increases directly with the mean distance. Hence the gas responsible for the sharp H and K lines must lie on the average at about half the distance of the stars, as if it were uniformly distributed in the intervening space. There is no doubt that these lines originate in interstellar space; but the gas must be regarded as rather irregularly distributed instead of having a constant density.

Following calcium, the next interstellar absorption lines to be discovered were the sodium D lines, also through their constant wavelengths in the spectra of spectroscopic binaries. With the development of high-dispersion coudé spectrographs at the Mt Wilson Observatory, further lines due to interstellar atoms were recognized; these are listed in the accompanying table.

WAVELENGTHS OF ATOMIC INTERSTELLAR LINES

Wavelength	Atom	Wavelength	Atom
3073·0	Ti II	3933·7	Ca II
3229·2	Ti II	3968·5	Ca II
3242·0	Ti II	4226·7	Ca I
3302·3	Na I	5890·0	Na I
3302·9	Na I	5895·9	Na I
3383·8	Ti II	7664·9	K I
3719·9	Fe I	7699·0	K I
3859·9	Fe I		

Titanium. The three lines due to ionized titanium discovered by Dunham call for special mention. Fig. 36 shows the Grotrian diagram of the Ti II multiplet to which two of the lines

K

belong. The dotted lines refer to the strongest transitions as observed in the laboratory. *These are not observed as interstellar lines.* The two lines that are observed, at wavelengths 3241, 3229, both arise from the lowest state (0). The line 3229 is one of the weakest in the laboratory. The identification would thus be unacceptable, even though the agreement in wavelength is very good, were it not for very sound physical reasons for the suppression of all lines arising from the higher energy levels.

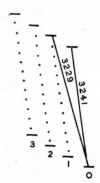

FIG. 36. Grotrian diagram of Ti II multiplet including two interstellar lines.

In the strange conditions of interstellar space we have gas at the extraordinarily low density of about 10^{-23} gm/cm^3. This gas is illuminated by very weak radiation from the stars. Consequently the chance of an atom either colliding with another atom or absorbing a quantum of starlight is vanishingly small. There will be a much greater tendency than usual for all the atoms to sink to the lowest level.

Now imagine a Ti II ion in the lowest state 0. After an interval of some weeks it may have the unusual experience of absorbing a quantum of radiation corresponding to one of the two lines 3241 or 3229. From the upper state it will immediately (after 10^{-8} seconds) fall back again emitting a permitted line; the ion will then be in one of the states 0, 1 or 2. If it is in state 1 or 2 it will again have to wait for some weeks before absorbing a quantum corresponding to one of the other (usually stronger) lines; it has a much greater probability – after only a few seconds – of falling back to state 0 via one or two 'forbidden' transitions. Thus there will be an extremely heavy concentration of ions in state 0 absorbing only the lines 3241 and 3229 in this multiplet.

The other Ti II lines identified by Dunham also arise from state 0. Thus the evidence for the four identifications is convincing, despite the gross departure from laboratory intensities.

In exactly the same way, the two interstellar lines of Fe I which have been observed arise from the lowest state of the Fe atom. In this case they correspond to very strong laboratory lines.

It is now clear that we can only hope to detect interstellar atoms by absorption lines if they happen to have resonance lines from the ground state in the accessible region of wavelengths. There is no hope of detecting interstellar absorption by such atoms as hydrogen, helium, oxygen, neon, etc., unless the barrier of terrestrial ozone can be penetrated. But such atoms reveal their presence as we have seen by emission lines.

The two lightest atoms with favourably placed resonance lines, lithium and ionized beryllium, have been looked for in vain in interstellar space.

Interstellar molecules. In just the same way as the Ti II multiplets are represented in skeleton form by the lines connected with state 0, so the *bands* which could be absorbed by interstellar molecules are reduced to a few isolated *lines* connected with the molecular state of lowest energy.

The Canadian astrophysicist A. McKellar was able to identify certain sharp interstellar lines observed by Adams at Mt Wilson Observatory with such skeletal remains of molecular bands; in some cases he predicted new lines before they were observed. The identified interstellar molecular lines are listed in the table on p. 148.

Temperature of interstellar space. The separate lines in a molecular band are due to the various energies of rotation that the molecule can possess (p. 54). There is one important exception to the rule that all interstellar absorption lines arise from the lowest level; the weak CN line 3874·00 arises from

WAVELENGTHS OF MOLECULAR INTERSTELLAR LINES

Wavelength	Molecule	Wavelength	Molecule
3143·2	CH I	3878·8	CH I
3579·0		3886·4	CH I
3745·3	CH II	3890·2	CH I
3874·0	CN I	3957·7	CH II
3874·6	CN I	4232·6	CH II
3875·8	CN I	4300·3	CH I

the *second* lowest level. From the relative intensity of 3874·00 to the neighbouring line 3874·62 McKellar computed how much rotational energy the interstellar CN molecules possess; from this he deduced a 'rotational temperature' of 2°·3 K for interstellar space.

Eddington had many years earlier computed a temperature of 3°·2 K from the density of energy in interstellar space. This is the temperature that would be read by a 'black' thermometer.

Interstellar space is so very far from conditions of thermodynamic equilibrium that temperature takes on very different values according to how it is defined. The radiation falling on matter, though very weak, is vastly richer in ultra-violet rays than ordinary radiation of temperature 2 to 3° K would be. Consequently the metals are mostly ionized and the free electrons have high velocities. The temperature measured by the velocity of electrons is about 10,000° K in H II regions, but falls to about 300° K where hydrogen is neutral (H I regions).

Unidentified diffuse lines. A number of diffuse lines or bands that must originate in interstellar space are listed in the table on p. 149.

The proof of the interstellar origin of these absorption lines does not lie in their constant wavelengths in spectroscopic binaries, because their measured wavelengths are necessarily inaccurate; for instance, the 4430 band is exceedingly broad (attaining a width of about 100 A) and so shallow that it was

WAVELENGTHS OF UNIDENTIFIED DIFFUSE
INTERSTELLAR BANDS

Wavelength
4430**
4760*
4890*
5780·5
5797·1
6180*
6203·0
6270·0
6283·9
6613·9

** Wings may be traced to ±75A
* Wings may be traced to ±30 A
See R. Wilson, *Ap. J.* **128**, 57, 1958

only discovered by spectrophotometry and can only be recognized on spectra that are greatly widened.

These diffuse lines are only found in distant Milky Way stars in which interstellar calcium and sodium lines are strong. However, measures of the 4430 band show a rather large scatter in the correlation with intensities of the other interstellar lines. The correlation is much stronger with *reddening* of starlight which is known to be interstellar in origin. If we observe a number of stars of a particular type, say B0, we find that all the near ones have about the same blue colour. However, faint B0 stars are progressively reddened as we go to greater distances. The phenomenon is somewhat similar to the reddening effect of haze upon the setting Sun, although the particles are very different in the two cases. The interstellar reddening is attributed to 'dust' or 'smoke' and not to the gas.

We therefore associate the unidentified diffuse lines with the dust rather than the gas. We know much more about the properties of the interstellar gas than of the dust, although attempts have been made to establish the character of the dust by measuring its absorption of distant starlight at many wavelengths from ultra-violet to infra-red. Distant starlight is also polarized by the dust. If these diffuse interstellar lines could be identified it would undoubtedly provide the most important clue as yet to the nature of the dust. It has been suggested that at the very low temperatures of interstellar space, solid crystals could give rise to absorption bands of about the width observed.

Structure of interstellar lines. Returning to the gas, the Ca II H and K lines were found by Beals to be double in certain stars (e.g. ρ Leonis). This suggested that in the particular direction of ρ Leonis we look through two separate concentrations of Ca II gas having different velocities. In high-dispersion coudé spectra Adams found that multiple components to interstellar lines are a common feature. Usually there is one component much stronger than all the others. The dominant component appears much the same in strength and velocity in two adjacent stars in the sky (which may be at very different distances from us), but the weak satellites may show conspicuous variations from star to star. One star is known with as many as seven components. Probably these faint components represent thin 'curtains' of gas that have been expelled from certain regions by the radiation pressure of hot stars. The dominant components appear to have their origin mostly in spiral arms of the Milky Way.

Interstellar lines and spiral structure. With the Mt Palomar 200-inch telescope Munch has found that there are two dominant components in the Ca II and Na I interstellar lines in the direction of the constellation Cassiopeia.[1]

In this direction we are looking about 45° away from the

[1] Adams' earlier work with the 100-inch telescope would undoubtedly have detected this doubling 10 years earlier but for the unfortunate circumstance that the 100-inch telescope is not mechanically designed to cover parts of the sky as near the pole as Cassiopeia.

direction of the Sun's galactic rotation about the centre C (fig. 37). Radial velocities there are sensitive to distances from the Sun. The two strong interstellar components suggest that in the direction of Cassiopeia there are two heavy concentrations of interstellar gas at very different distances from the Sun. It is tempting to associate these with two *spiral arms*. This is one of the most promising approaches to the problem of spiral structure from spectroscopic observations.[1]

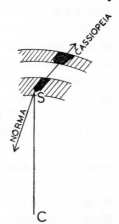

FIG. 37. Doubling of interstellar lines and spiral structure. In the directions of Cassiopeia and Norma we look through two concentrations of gas at very different distances from the Sun S.

The hydrogen 21 cm line. Although radiation of wavelength longer than 20,000 A (or 0·0002 cm) lies outside the range of ordinary optical spectroscopy, brief mention must be made of the hydrogen 21 cm line first detected by radio telescopes in 1951.

Spectroscopic interest is attached to this discovery because it was on the basis of knowledge of energy levels of the neutral H atom that H. C. van der Hulst predicted as early as 1944 that conditions in interstellar space favoured the emission of radiation at about 21 cm. It only required the post-war development of suitable radio telescopes to confirm van der Hulst's prediction.

The hydrogen atom is known to be cosmically the most abundant of all. Very roughly the H I regions (of neutral

[1] The first indication of these two spiral arms came from spectroscopic determinations of distance by W. W. Morgan and his colleagues at Yerkes Observatory, using groups of early type stars involved in diffuse nebulae as tracers of spiral structure. Similar doubling of interstellar lines has been found at the Radcliffe Observatory in a few distant stars in the direction of the southern constellation Norma.

hydrogen) occupy 90 per cent of space in the Milky Way. Thus throughout the greater part of the Milky Way we have interstellar H I, with a complete concentration in the ground state, as with other atoms. But the ground state is double. The H atom is of course composed of a single proton and a single electron, each spinning; the spins may be either parallel or anti-parallel, and there is a minute difference in energy between the two states. Transitions between the two states are forbidden by the ordinary selection rules, but interstellar conditions favour the downward transition accompanied by the emission of the 21 cm line.

The 21 cm line has been very intensively studied all along the Milky Way, especially in Holland and Australia, and has proved to be a most fruitful means of investigating spiral structure. It is of interest to note that the 21 cm line is emitted by neutral hydrogen, while the diffuse nebulae recorded on direct photographs or with nebular spectrographs refer to H II regions where ionized hydrogen is capturing free electrons. We believe the gas to be mainly concentrated in the spiral arms, whether neutral or ionized. If this were not so, radio and optical observations of the gas would refer to quite different regions of space.

The 21 cm line (the only line radiation so far detected by radio telescopes) is subject to Doppler shifts just like the lines used in optical spectroscopy. Very large Doppler shifts are observed, the more so because radiation of these long wavelengths passes essentially unobstructed by the dust that hampers all optical work; consequently, radio telescopes will record essentially *all* the 21 cm radiation from a given direction coming from any part of the Milky Way and even beyond. The difficulty is to determine at what distance is located the main source of 21 cm radiation with a particular Doppler shift.

A map of the Milky Way indicating rather circular spiral

structure has been drawn up from combining northern and southern observations of the 21 cm line. The problem of locating spiral arms at a particular distance from the Sun has been met in part by utilizing the ordinary spectroscopic observations of galactic rotation (p. 94).

A recent radio observation of the greatest importance by J. H. Oort and his colleagues has been that of an expanding spiral arm close to the centre of the Milky Way, where optical telescopes have little hope of penetrating the screen of interstellar dust.

Chapter 11

UNSTABLE AND PULSATING STARS

New stars (novae). The sudden appearance of a bright star where none had been seen before naturally aroused consternation among early astronomers who regarded the 'fixed stars' as unchanging. Speculations about the origin of these novae gradually turned to physical reasoning as spectroscopic observations began to accumulate at the beginning of the pre-

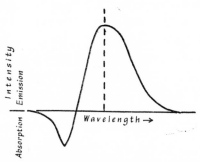

FIG. 38. Profile of combined emission and absorption in the spectrum of a nova.

sent century. Nova Persei (1901), Nova Geminorum (1912) and Nova Aquilae (1918) were important in this respect.

Spectra of novae at maximum light and during decline are extremely complicated. But one general feature needs description at the outset. Emission bands appear after maximum, many angstroms wide, and each band is accompanied by diffuse absorption on the violet edge. The 'profile' of such a combination of absorption and emission is sketched in fig. 38.

154

The dotted vertical line indicates the undisplaced wavelength of the original spectrum line.

The explanation of this typical profile is shown diagrammatically in fig. 39.

The central star is visualized as having blown off a vast shell of gas on all sides. The shaded area of this shell lies between the star and the observer. This part is absorbing light from the star beneath. The absorption has a large Doppler shift to the violet because it is the part of the shell approaching the

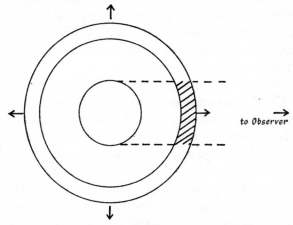

to Observer

FIG. 39. Expanding shell around a nova.

observer most rapidly. The rest of the shell is partly approaching and partly receding from the observer. It produces the wide band of emission on either side of the undisplaced wavelength. Theoretically, this model predicts that the red edge of the emission band will be cut off, because the part of the shell moving most rapidly from the observer is obscured by the star, but this is difficult to detect.

Strong support for this model of an outward explosion of gas is given by the fact that several novae have been observed to be surrounded by outward moving gaseous fragments.

This debris only becomes visible after the lapse of considerable time (a year or more) following maximum light; soon after maximum the gas is too close to the star, and the star is still too bright, for the telescope to resolve them.

It is not surprising that such debris is not distributed perfectly symmetrically about the nova. Instead we are often driven to picture jets of gas shot out in certain preferred directions. Some novae (Nova Pictoris, 1925; Nova Herculis, 1934) appear to be resolved into two distinct components for a time. Such irregularities need not vitiate the general interpretation of profiles like that of fig. 38 in terms of expanding gases. The bright and dark bands do in fact often exhibit irregularities that could be attributed to expansion of the gas in certain preferred directions.

Spectroscopic development of novae. McLaughlin has compared the development of a number of novae with well-observed spectra, and recognizes the following typical stages:

(*a*) *The pre-maximum spectrum* is rarely observed because the increase in light to maximum takes place so rapidly (only a few hours in some cases); the few spectra that have been obtained consist primarily of absorption lines (indicating spectral types ranging from B5 to F2) displaced to the violet.

(*b*) *The principal spectrum*, which is prominent at maximum light, resembles the absorption spectrum of a supergiant A or F star. The violet shift is larger than that of (*a*). Emission lines, displaced to the red, begin to appear after maximum light.

(*c*) *The diffuse-enhanced spectrum* has a still larger violet shift for the absorption lines; both bright and dark bands are characterized by great width.

(*d*) *The Orion spectrum* is characterized by higher temperature lines (He I, O II, N II) and still higher velocities than those of the previous systems. This feature is visible during the declining phases in light – usually from 1 to 4 magnitudes below maximum. (The name is derived from the similarity to the spectra of the bright early-type B stars forming the constellation of Orion.)

(*e*) *The nebular stage:* as the star fades, the continuous spectrum which has been prominent hitherto, drops out and new emission lines appear. The nebulium pair of [O III] usually appears, but with intensities that vary from nova to nova. [O III] 4363 is about as strong as the nebulium pair. (In the diffuse nebulae and the planetaries [O III] 4363 is relatively weak.)

The picture presented by these observations is one of ejection of gas with progressively increasing velocity from the central star. The corresponding shells of gases must therefore be intermingling as the later ejecta, with higher velocities, catch up, pass and obscure the earlier debris.

Extensive measures of the bright and dark lines, and of how they change with time have been made in the spectra of several novae. The total number of radiating atoms in the shells can be computed if the distance of the nova is known. The change in volume of the expanding shells and the densities of the ions (with the help of ionization theory) can also be computed. These necessarily rough calculations give us some idea of the *mass* of a typical nova shell; the mass turns out to be only a very small fraction (about 10^{-5}) of the total mass of the nova. This suggests that the outburst of a nova need not necessarily involve any very permanent change in the star. In fact we find that most novae do settle down after the outburst into stars of much the same brightness as before.

Several novae have suffered recurrent outbursts at intervals of a few decades. Examples are T Coronae Borealis (1866, 1946), RS Ophiuchi (1898, 1933, 1958). T Coronae Borealis is of particular interest in that after exhibiting the spectrum of an ordinary nova during decline, at minimum the spectrum is composite; superposed on the spectrum of a cool M type star appear the hot features of H and He bright lines. This need not be due to the presence of two stars. In the case of Nova Herculis 1934 and Nova Pictoris 1925 temporary duplicity reported by double star observers seems to have referred to condensations within the expanding shells. However, Nova Herculis has recently been found to show light variations like an eclipsing binary with a period of 4·65 hours. This nova is of unique spectroscopic interest in that Baade found quite different distributions of [N II] and [O III] radiation in the elliptical disk.

Supernovae. While ordinary novae reach absolute magnitudes of about −7 to −8 at maximum, the rarer *supernovae* are 7 or 8 magnitudes brighter still. For a short time these objects radiate a few per cent of the total radiation of a whole galaxy.

After recognition of supernovae as a class distinct from ordinary novae, strenuous attempts were made by Zwicky, Minkowski and others to obtain spectra quickly after discovery. A supernova occurs only once in 200 to 400 years per galaxy on the average; all spectra so far obtained refer to faint objects in distant extragalactic nebulae. Much remains to be learnt.

Supernovae are divided into two classes according to their spectra and light-curves. Type I (with absolute magnitude about −16) have spectra with very broad bright bands; the widths correspond to gas velocities of about 4000 km/sec if interpreted as Doppler effects of expansion. Attempts to identify these bands have so far failed, although there is some evidence for [O I] 6300, 6364. Type II (with absolute magnitude −14 or less) have spectra which are more easily understood in terms of particularly violent ordinary novae. In one of the best spectra secured (by Mayall in 1948) two sets of hydrogen absorption lines could be recognized, one with small velocity, the other with an expansion velocity of 5700 km/sec.

Of the three recognized supernovae within the Milky Way (all occurring before the era of spectroscopy), the Crab nebula is of special importance because the remnants of the explosion (recorded by the Chinese in A.D. 1054) are still easily observable. The spectrum consists of a continuum and bright lines due to H, He I, [O II], [O III], [N II], [Ne III] and [S II]. The continuous spectrum originates in an amorphous mass and is strongly polarized. The bright line spectrum arises in narrow *filaments* which can be isolated on photographs taken through suitable colour filters. Although not very dissimilar to spectra of filamentary nebulae found elsewhere in the Galaxy, hydrogen does appear to be rather weak in the Crab nebula.

Early attempts to explain the strong continuous spectrum led to a mass for the nebula of about 36 Suns. However, if the continuum originates in 'synchrotron radiation' emitted by electrons accelerated in magnetic fields the estimate of the mass is greatly reduced.

Rates of development of ordinary novae. There is a fairly close parallelism between the rate of spectroscopic development of ordinary novae, the rate of changes in light and the changes in velocity. Fast novae (N Lacertae 1936) have the highest velocities (1500 to 2000 km/sec); slow novae (N Herculis 1934, N Pictoris 1925) the smallest (400 km/sec).

Slow novae also tend to show the sharpest lines. Presumably the great widths of the lines in the fast novae are due to Doppler broadening and to large turbulent velocities. The smaller velocities of ejection associated with the slow novae indicate less turbulence. This makes the slow novae far simpler objects for study. Further, the slow rate of development makes it much easier to obtain a complete observational record.

The slow nova N Pictoris 1925 showed strong lines due to [Fe VI], [Fe VII] some years after maximum; the identification of these highly ionized forms of Fe provided an important clue to the later identification of [Fe X], [Fe XIII], [Fe XIV] in the solar corona (p. 236). Another slow nova RR Telescopii, at maximum from 1944 to 1948, is progressing through the nebular stage at about one seventh the speed of N Pictoris. In 1958 all stages from [Fe II] to [Fe VII] were represented simultaneously.[1] The progressive increase in ionization is typical of this stage of novae. Presumably the ejected gases are subjected to increasing ionization through diminishing pressure, with the most highly ionized gases furthest out. This is the reverse of the situation in planetary nebulae, where the highest ionization occurs near the nucleus.

The slowest nova on record is the remarkable star η Carinae. Known to vary between 2nd and 4th magnitude between 1680 and 1830, it became for a time around 1841 the second brightest star in the sky, since when it has faded below naked-eye visibility.

The spectrum of η Carinae is marked by extraordinarily strong emission lines of [Fe II], first identified by Merrill shortly after the identification of the nebulium lines with [O III]. Displaced absorption is also present. The star is surrounded by a gaseous halo in which expansion from year to year has been detected. Various lines of evidence point to η Carinae being situated within a conspicuous diffuse nebula (John Herschel's 'Keyhole' Nebula) at a distance of about 2 kiloparsecs. This would mean that at maximum η Carinae had an absolute magnitude of about -13 or -14 which it was able to maintain for a space of several years. This implies that η Carinae must be regarded as a supernova, but of a different class from those of Types I and II. The surrounding halo is strongly polarized, but the polarization seems to have a different origin from that in the Crab nebula. The presence

[1] Including several lines due to [Fe IV] never previously observed in any celestial object, nor in the laboratory.

of forbidden lines *in absorption* seems to point to the presence of strong electric fields.

Continuous ejection. Many stars appear to be ejecting gases continuously. The nova P Cygni reached 2nd magnitude in 1600 and is still of 4th magnitude. Most lines in the spectrum of P Cygni have profiles of the form of fig. 38, which have in fact come to be termed 'P Cyg profiles'. The velocities of ejection from P Cygni stars are about 100 to 200 km/sec, i.e. considerably less than those found in novae. The star AG Carinae, with P Cygni spectrum, is of special interest because, unlike P Cygni itself, it shows a surrounding ring nebula. The P Cygni spectrum must arise close to the star, but nevertheless the surrounding nebula is probably derived from matter originally ejected from the star.

α *Cygni.* This 1st magnitude star is of supergiant A2 type. Although early observations showed only absorption lines, the discovery of weak emission at Hα with violet-displaced absorption of P Cygni type was of great importance. Probably this supergiant is ejecting matter on a gentle scale, perhaps not sufficiently violently for it to escape permanently. Numerous measures of radial velocity show that the atmosphere is continuously disturbed. The radial velocity measured on one plate gives a deceptive idea of the accuracy with which the velocity *of the star* can be measured. The average of many measures (which scatter with a total range of 15 km/sec) will still not refer to the velocity of the star if there is a greater tendency for outward-moving atoms to absorb than for inward-moving atoms.

There is some evidence that *all* stars of high luminosity lying in the top right-hand corner of the Hertzsprung–Russell diagram are subject to irregular disturbances similar to those observed in α Cygni.

Cepheid variables. These variable stars of supergiant F or G type show periodic changes in type and radial velocity in

L

phase with the variations in light. The periods range from about 2 to 50 days.

The rise to maximum light occurs faster than the subsequent decline. The velocity curve is a close mirror-image of the light-curve (fig. 40), maximum velocity of approach coinciding with maximum light, at which time the spectral type is earliest.

Several attempts have been made to explain Cepheid variables in terms of two stars. But the light-curve cannot be explained in terms of eclipses (where minimum light should

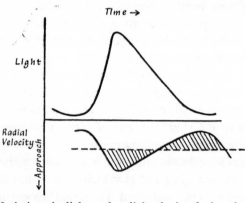

Fig. 40. Variations in light and radial velocity during the cycle of a Cepheid variable.

occur when the velocity is near its average value). Further, the characteristic shape of the velocity-curve indicates an eccentric orbit with periastron always occurring near the point furthest from the terrestrial observer.

It is generally accepted that the variations in light of the Cepheid variables are due to the periodic pulsations of a single star. The origin is probably to be traced to some deep-seated source within the star, the tap of energy-production being periodically turned on and off.

The study of high-dispersion spectra of Cepheid variables

throughout their light-curves is one that deserves to be prosecuted further. It seems likely that a shock-wave passes through the atmosphere during each cycle. Different lines are formed at different depths within the atmosphere, and accurate comparison of the behaviour of different lines through a cycle can thus throw light on the physical nature of the pulsation near the surface. There is some evidence that velocities derived from lines formed high and low in the atmosphere differ by as much as 3 or 4 km/sec. It has been recently discovered that the Ca II H and K lines appear in emission at certain phases in some Cepheids.

RR Lyrae variables. These variable stars have periods between 0·2 and 1·0 days with characteristics rather similar to those of Cepheid variables and must also be regarded as single pulsating stars. Their absolute magnitudes are about +0·5, considerably fainter than the Cepheids. Few are found brighter than 10th apparent magnitude and it is difficult to follow the rapid spectroscopic changes in such faint stars. However, their spectra are receiving much current attention because they show peculiarities which set them apart in the ordinary scheme of classification. The strength of metal lines places them in class A, while other criteria involving the hydrogen lines or the G band place them in class F.

RR Lyrae variables are found in great numbers within globular clusters, as well as in the general field of stars. Those in the general field have high velocities, like the globular clusters, and are found well out of the plane of the Milky Way.

W Virginis. This is the type-star of a group of variables which like the RR Lyrae variables are found in globular clusters and out of the plane of the Milky Way.

W Virginis is the only member of the group bright enough for detailed spectroscopic study. It shows bright hydrogen lines shortly before maximum light. But the most remarkable feature lies in a doubling of the lines at maximum. The violet component of the double persists (with smaller displacement) after maximum, while the red component disappears. The velocity of the original violet component continues to change in such a manner that it becomes the red component at the next maximum.

These facts suggest that the fundamental period is twice the period (14 days) of the light-variations. The hypothesis of two stars is not perhaps ruled out quite so conclusively as in classical Cepheids. But a more easily acceptable explanation is that we are dealing with two concentric shells alternately rising and falling above the star. Shortly after these two shells have collided the bright lines (whose origin is attributed to the collision) are observed with a velocity corresponding to the rising shell. The falling shell soon sinks into invisibility after the collision.

It would be highly desirable to confirm this provisional model with further observations.

Long-period variables. These variable stars are quite different from Cepheids in having periods ranging from about 100 to 600 days and spectra of M type (or more rarely N and S types). They are cool giants whose light variations do not repeat themselves with strict regularity.

Although the best known variable of this type, Mira Ceti, has a strange B type companion which can only be detected at minimum light, it appears that most long-period variables are single stars, pulsating like Cepheids.

Spectroscopically, the long-period variables are full of interest. In combination with the low-temperature M type spectrum, bright lines due to hydrogen, Fe, Si, Mg, etc. appear with varying intensities through the cycle.

The intensities of the hydrogen Balmer lines, which normally decrease regularly along the series, are quite anomalous. But this has been very satisfactorily explained. The origin of the bright lines appears to be *below* that of the dark lines. For instance, Hε, which lies close to the strong absorption line Ca II 3968, is very weak; it must be weakened by overlying Ca II gas. Hα and Hβ are weakened by molecular Ti O absorption in the M type variables, but are nearly normal in intensity in N and S variables with Ti O inconspicuous or absent. On high dispersion the rather wide hydrogen emission can be seen to be cut up by several narrow absorption lines each of which may be identified with some overlying atom. Within Hδ, for instance, the resonance line of indium appears. The other resonance line of indium at 4511 A (having the same upper state) appears bright at some phases. The origin of this bright line can be confidently attributed to fluorescent excitation by Hδ emission. This phenomenon is an exact parallel of Bowen's fluorescent mechanism in planetary nebulae (p. 138). Another remarkable case of fluorescence in long-period variables is provided by the lines Fe 4202, 4308 which appear as strong bright lines even when other lines *in the same multiplet* remain dark. The selective excitation of these lines is satisfactorily explained by postulating that the resonance line Mg II 2795, which coincides with another Fe line, is a strong bright line.[1] Herbig has recently identified a number of emission lines with fragments of molecular Al H bands. Here the selective excitation does not seem to have a fluorescent origin.

The origin of the primary emission of H, Mg II, etc. is still somewhat obscure. The most promising suggestion is that it is connected with a rising convective layer in which the hydrogen atoms are half ionized. The successive ionization and recombination of the abundant H atoms induces convection currents. At the top of the convective layer, ionized hydrogen

---

[1] This line lies too far to the ultra-violet to be directly observed. However, recent spectra of the Sun taken from high-altitude rockets have shown a strong bright core within the solar absorption line.

(which has stored energy from the interior) captures free electrons and emits the Balmer series in the process. The fluorescent mechanism demands very low pressures and probably takes place at a level well above the origin of the hydrogen lines.

There is some direct observational evidence that during the cycle the hydrogen emission, at first at a very low level, gradually rises upwards from the star. In Mira Ceti, the bright lines are shifted by some 10 km/sec to the violet relative to the dark lines at maximum light. This difference becomes smaller during the decline to minimum.

Careful analysis of high-dispersion spectra of some long-period variables has revealed the presence of highly interesting heavy elements. The most remarkable of these is the unstable element technetium, identified by Merrill in R Andromedae. Rare-earths such as neodymium and samarium are also represented by numerous lines in this star.

One feature of long-period variables which deserves more attention concerns the formation and dissociation of molecules. At minimum, the temperature of the atmosphere is lower (judged by the absorption lines), the molecular bands are stronger, and an unexplained general veiling of the spectrum occurs. It is possible that the temperature is low enough locally for solid particles to form.

Irregular variables. Most M type giants show irregular variations in light and radial velocity. The two best studied cases are α Orionis (Betelgeuse) and α Herculis. In the spectra some lines are double. There is good reason to suppose that the violet components arise in enormous circumstellar shells expanding outwards with a velocity of about 10 km/sec. α Herculis has a companion star which also shows the circumstellar lines in its spectrum. It is deduced that the shell envelopes *both stars* and has a diameter at least 20,000 times that of the Sun.

Stars that vary intrinsically (apart from the variations due to eclipses discussed in Chapter 8) are quite numerous and are found among nearly every known spectral class. Variability is probably a more frequent occurrence among luminous stars than among stars like the Sun or fainter. Nevertheless, 'flare stars' among faint M dwarfs are known; these stars are occasionally seen to brighten in the course of a few minutes. The few spectra that have been obtained show bright lines of hydrogen and calcium rather reminiscent of chromospheric eruptions on the Sun; a continuous spectrum strong in the blue has also been observed which has not yet been explained. Some faint irregular variables, like those forming the T Tauri group, have a tendency to be found in regions of interstellar dust. Here again the origin of the variations is not understood.

Chapter 12

SPECTROSCOPIC DETERMINATION
OF DISTANCE

The accurate determination of the distances of stars and other celestial objects is one of the most difficult problems in astronomy and astrophysics. Compared with the accuracy with which positions and motions within the solar system can be measured, the inaccuracies that have to be tolerated in stellar distances are most disappointing. However, the rough methods that have to be employed have sufficed to give us a much clearer idea of the universe than that held 100 or even 40 years ago. These rough methods distinguish with certainty between objects like planetary and diffuse nebulae lying within the Milky Way and the spiral galaxies lying right outside. The spectroscope has played a dominant role in the setting up of a cosmic distance scale, and new techniques are continually being developed to refine the whole process of measuring astronomical distances.

Trigonometrical parallaxes. This fundamental approach, based on the apparent oscillation of stars' positions due to the Earth's orbital motion, gives us the distances of the nearest stars in terms of the Earth's distance from the Sun. An accuracy of 2 or 3 per cent is achieved in the most favourable cases. But the relative inaccuracy increases directly with the distance. At distances of about 100 parsecs the method fails. When we recall that the Sun is about 9000 parsecs from the centre of the Milky Way, it will be appreciated what an

168

insignificant part of the Milky Way can be surveyed by the method of trigonometrical parallaxes. Beyond 100 parsecs we have to rely heavily upon the spectroscope.

Spectroscopic parallaxes. Sir William Herschel's pioneer survey of the Milky Way depended on assuming that all stars had the same luminosity as the Sun. This of course is now known to be far from true. Instead, we assume that all stars with identical spectra have the same luminosity. The problem of measuring distances with the spectroscope then reduces to the problem of calibrating absolute magnitudes for each spectral type and luminosity class (see p. 63). For dwarfs of type F to M this calibration is easy because we have accurate trigonometrical parallaxes for the nearby stars from which we can build up an HR diagram with a well-defined main sequence (fig. 15, p. 66). Once the absolute magnitude M is known, the apparent magnitude m enables us to calculate the star's distance by a well-known relation.[1] It must be noted that this relation in its simplest form attributes all the dimming of starlight to distance, as if space were perfectly transparent. However, we know that the light of stars at distances of several hundred parsecs is often greatly dimmed by intervening dust. The difficult problem of correcting for this interstellar absorption will be considered later.

It is far more difficult to calibrate absolute magnitudes for the O, B and A stars, the giants and supergiants than for main sequence stars of types F to K. For these bright stars we have to rely on less direct methods than that of trigonometrical parallaxes. We now consider various methods in turn.

Star clusters. Scattered over the sky we find numerous

---

[1] $5 \log r = -5 \log \pi = m - M + 5$, where r is the distance in parsecs, and π is the spectroscopic parallax in seconds of arc. $m - M$, called the *distance modulus*, is frequently used by astronomers as a measure of distance.

clusters of stars that must form physically related groups. Provided they do not cover too large an area of the sky we can treat all members of a cluster as being at the same distance from us. A few stars may not be members of the cluster and happen to lie in the foreground or background. But since a cluster must be formed of stars moving together, in order to preserve its identity, the non-members can be distinguished by their failure to share the same radial velocity or proper motion.

If we observe and classify spectra of as many stars as possible in a cluster and plot their spectral classes against their

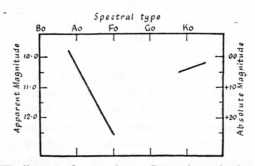

FIG. 41. HR diagram of a star cluster. Spectral type is plotted against apparent magnitude; if the absolute magnitude is known for one spectral type it can be deduced for all others represented.

apparent magnitude, we obtain a portion of a Hertzsprung–Russell diagram such as fig. 41. In this diagram we recognize a main sequence extending from B8 to F0 and a few K type giants. Now we know from fig. 15 that the absolute magnitude of an F0 dwarf is $+2.5$. Suppose for example that the F0 dwarfs in the cluster had an apparent magnitude 12.5; then we deduce $m - M = 10.0$ and the distance of the cluster is 1000 parsecs (3260 light years). Having begun with ordinates in apparent magnitudes only, we can now deduce absolute magnitudes for all stars in the cluster, including some B stars and K giants for which no trigonometrical parallaxes are reliable.

By exactly the same reasoning, double stars can be used to measure differences in absolute magnitude of stars of various spectral classes.

Moving clusters. If a cluster is sufficiently near to us to show perceptible proper motion, the combination of the proper motions, radial velocities and spectral classes is particularly powerful in establishing absolute magnitudes. The fundamental assumption is that the motions of all stars in the cluster are strictly parallel in space.

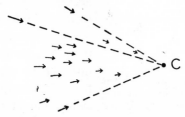

FIG. 42. Proper motions of a moving cluster. The motion of each star across the sky in a given time is represented by an arrow in the present position of the star. All stars move towards the convergent point *C* due to perspective. The stars with the smallest proper motions have the largest radial velocities (recession) and vice versa.

If the cluster covers an appreciable area of the sky, then the proper motions will tend to converge or diverge from a certain point (see fig. 42). The best example is provided by a group of naked-eye stars in the constellation Taurus known as the Hyades. The convergent point is known with considerable accuracy. The direction from the Earth to this convergent point is, through perspective, the actual direction of motion in space of the cluster. Since the motions are converging the cluster must be receding from us. This is confirmed by the radial velocities.

Fig. 43 shows how the distance of every member of the

Hyades with accurately known radial velocity and proper motion can be determined. A star S seen from O is shifted to the direction OS' after the lapse of one year. The direction of motion SS' is known to be parallel to OC (the direction to the convergent point). Hence we know both angles $SS'O$ and SOS'. The radial velocity tells us how far the star travels ($S'N$) in one year in the line of sight. It is then a matter of simple geometry to deduce the distance of the star OS.[1]

The Hyades contains a few K giants whose absolute mag-

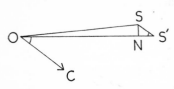

FIG. 43. Determination of the distance of a star in a moving cluster from radial velocity and proper motion.

nitudes can be determined accurately in this way. Unfortunately there are no main sequence stars of type earlier than A1, so that this does not take us very high up in the HR diagram where the calibration of absolute magnitudes is most urgently needed.

In the southern hemisphere there is a vast collection of B stars stretching over some 50° of the sky which appear to be moving together in the so-called Scorpio–Centaurus stream. Proper motions and radial velocities have been measured in considerable numbers, and while the proper motions are not particularly accurate, this moving cluster has been used with considerable success to determine absolute magnitudes of main sequence B stars. In fact, the calibration of absolute magnitudes for B stars rests rather heavily on the Scorpio–Centaurus stream.

[1] The distance in parsecs is $\dfrac{V \tan \lambda}{4 \cdot 74 \mu}$ where V is the radial velocity (km/sec), μ is the proper motion (seconds of arc per annum,) i.e. angle SON, λ is the angle SOC.

Statistical parallaxes. Proper motions and radial velocities can be combined rather similarly to measure absolute magnitudes even when the stars concerned are not moving together in parallel paths as a cluster.

Suppose we select all stars classed as B5V in a fairly narrow range of apparent magnitude. We assume as usual that all stars so classified have the same absolute magnitude; the restriction on the apparent magnitude will then ensure that all the selected stars will be at about the same distance. Considering the stars in one plane they will tend to lie on a circle centred on the observer *O* as in fig. 44.

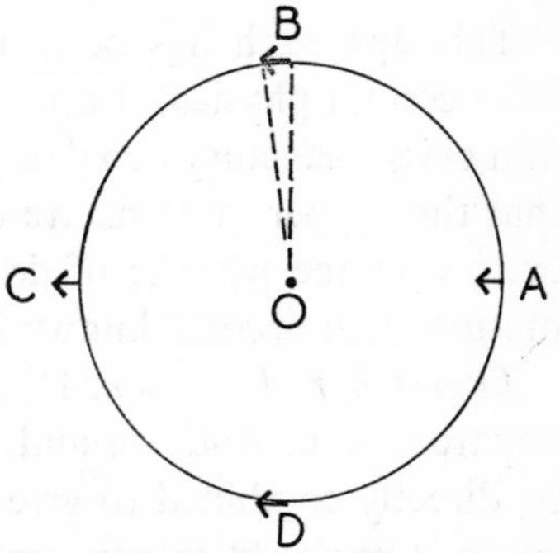

FIG. 44. Statistical parallaxes. In a group of stars lying at about the same distance from *O*, with the same average speed relative to *O*, the spectroscope shows the average speed (in km/sec) in directions *A*, *C*; combination with the proper motions in directions *B*, *D* yields the average distance of the group.

We already saw (p. 90) that the Sun is moving towards Hercules at the rate of 20 km/sec relative to the nearby stars. Now every B5 star will have its own peculiar motion, but if we take a sufficiently great number of *unrelated* B5 stars we may assume that their average peculiar motion will be zero.

In the direction *A* we observe our B5 stars with an average radial velocity of −20 km/sec, and an average proper motion of zero. Similarly in direction *C*, we find radial velocities of +20 km/sec and zero proper motions on the average.

In directions *B* and *D* the radial velocities tend to cancel out, but we find a certain average proper motion indicated by the small angle. Provided the peculiar motions average zero, we may say that the average motion at B and D is 20 km/sec relative to O. The measured angular cross-motion can only correspond to 20 km/sec at one distance. This distance is then the radius of the circle, or the average distance of the selected stars. Knowing the apparent magnitudes, we immediately deduce the mean absolute magnitude of the group.

This approach has been applied to many objects which have certain physical properties, e.g. variable stars of a certain class, planetary nebulae, etc. Its weakness lies in the fact that the proper motions are often poorly determined. However, with the passage of decades and centuries the proper motions will become known increasingly accurately.

Interstellar absorption. Hitherto we have assumed that an apparent magnitude m and an absolute magnitude M can be directly combined to give the distance. This implies that space is perfectly transparent, which is not true owing to the presence of interstellar dust and gas.[1] Can we measure how much any particular star is dimmed by the interstellar matter?

Distant stars near the galactic plane are reddened by the dust. Thus a distant B0 star may have the colour of an A or F star. If we have a measure (preferably photo-electric) of the colour of a star, and we know its spectrum, we can deduce the *colour excess* or amount of reddening, to be attributed to the intervening dust. Much work has been done on the relationship between colour excess and the total dimming of starlight. At present it may be claimed that we have a fairly reliable method of measuring the dimming from colours and spectral types. But there is room for improvement, especially in determining the true colours of supergiants. Further, there

---

[1] Fortunately the error is negligible for stars near enough for their trigonometrical parallaxes to be accurately measured. The fundamental calibration of spectroscopic parallaxes is thus unaffected.

are misgivings that the law of reddening is not exactly the same in different directions within the Milky Way. The dust that provides the obstruction could consist of needle-shaped grains, oriented by a weak general magnetic field in the Galaxy;[1] if this were so, we would be looking along the needles in one direction and across them in another.

Suppose, however, that we know the true law of reddening and that we deduce from a star's colour and spectral type that the star's light has been dimmed by a magnitudes in its passage to us. The star of *apparent* magnitude m would appear of magnitude $m - a$ if the obstruction could be removed. The *corrected distance modulus* $m - a - M$ is the measure that we require for determining its distance after allowance for the interstellar absorption.[2]

Interstellar lines. In the spectra of early B stars, the presence of interstellar Ca II or Na I lines is always an indication that we are observing distant stars through a considerable depth of gas. If the gas were distributed perfectly uniformly then the intensities of the interstellar lines would give a direct measure of the distance of the stars lying behind the gas. However, the gas is strongly concentrated in the plane of the Milky Way so that for stars at galactic latitude 20° or more the lines become weak or invisible; moreover, the gas is patchily distributed within the galactic plane so that one cannot expect a strict proportionality of intensity to distance. Finally, the Doppler shifts due to galactic rotation complicate the relationship between the intensities of the interstellar lines and distance.

Despite these complications it has been possible to

---

[1] This state of affairs is suggested by observations of the polarization of starlight.

[2] In the presence of absorption the equation in the footnote to p. 169 must be amended to read

$$5 \log r = m - a - M + 5$$

determine rough distances from the interstellar lines. The method has been especially useful for novae.

The broad unidentified interstellar band at 4430 A can also be used in this way for determining distances. It is so wide that it is free from appreciable broadening due to galactic rotation.

Galactic rotation. As we have seen (Chap. 6), radial velocities of distant objects vary with galactic longitude, due to the differential rotation of the Galaxy, the amplitude of the variation being proportional to the mean distance of the objects. In order to discover the law of rotation we must first know the distances of the stars exhibiting the effects of galactic rotation. The law of rotation is established mainly through observations of B stars and Cepheids whose distances are known, although the accuracy could be improved considerably.

It is now possible to turn the argument round and to use the known law of rotation to establish distances for other objects whose distances are less reliably known. For instance, radial velocities of N type stars exhibit galactic rotation to an extent that indicates an absolute magnitude of −2·3 for these stars. The method is useful for establishing absolute magnitudes and distances of the relatively rare supergiants. All distances determined in this way are on the assumed scale of distances for the B stars and Cepheids.

The velocities of neutral hydrogen measured with radio telescopes through the 21 cm line are transformed into distances by assuming a law of rotation for the whole Galaxy. The tracing of spiral arms in the Galaxy through radio observations depends essentially on this method. The model used in the radio analysis is thus based primarily on optical observations, and to a large extent on spectroscopic observations. The scale again rests mainly on the scale of distances deduced for such objects as the B type stars and Cepheid variables.

Nova parallaxes. Another striking example of the measurement of distance by combining radial velocities and cross-motions is provided by the expanding nebulosities found around many novae.

At the time of the outburst we observe P Cygni profiles indicating the ejection of shells with a certain velocity V km/sec. Some t years later we may observe a small expanding nebula surrounding the nova, separated from it by d seconds of arc. We identify this with the shell ejected with the highest velocity and assume this is the same as the largest velocity formerly observed in absorption in the P Cygni profile (V). The distance travelled in the line of sight is known (it is $Vt \times 3\cdot16 \times 10^7$ km, the numerical factor being the number of seconds in a year); the distance travelled across the line of sight is $Rd/2\cdot06 \times 10^5$, where R is the required distance of the nova in km (the numerical factor here being the number of seconds of arc in a radian). Equating these two distances we find $R = 6\cdot48 \times 10^{12}Vt/d$ km, or $Vt/4\cdot74d$ parsecs.

It is to be noted that the calculation assumes that the velocity V is maintained unchanged over a period of years, although it is possible that in some novae the ejected gases are decelerated in their outward passage by collision with surrounding gases.

An important feature of this method of measuring stellar distances is that no use is made of the star's apparent brightness; the method is thus independent of any interstellar absorption. Beyond the range of trigonometrical parallaxes, it is the uncertainties regarding interstellar absorption that set the chief obstacle to accurate measurement of stellar distances.

Period-Luminosity law. Cepheid variables are the most important distance-indicators of all because (*a*) according to the Period-Luminosity law (discovered in the Magellanic Clouds, where all Cepheids can be treated as at the same distance) it is only necessary to find the period of a Cepheid to know its

M

absolute magnitude and hence its distance, (b) Cepheids can be recognized in many of the nearer extragalactic nebulae.

However, before using this method for absolute distances we must know either the distance of the Magellanic Clouds, or fix the zero-point of the Period-Luminosity law by measuring the distances of Cepheids in the Galaxy. Moreover, it is very difficult to allow correctly for interstellar absorption in measuring the distances of galactic Cepheids, for they are nearly all appreciably reddened and there is still considerable doubt as to the true colour of a Cepheid.

The zero-point was originally established by means of statistical parallaxes of galactic Cepheids. But the proper motions were weakly determined, and it is now known that the Cepheids are more luminous than originally supposed. Many approaches are currently being used to calibrate the Period-Luminosity law more accurately. It has recently been discovered that a few galactic Cepheids are members of open clusters whose distances can be found independently.

Pulsation parallaxes. An ingenious method of measuring distances of Cepheids, originally proposed by Baade in 1928, is based on the accepted model of pulsation for these variables.

In Chapter 4 (p. 62) we saw how we can calculate a star's radius if its temperature and distance were known, for Stefan's law gives the total radiation (or absolute magnitude) as a function of radius and temperature. For pulsating Cepheids we can calculate the radius independently of the distance, and use Stefan's law to derive the distance.

The observational data required are (a) apparent magnitudes at maximum and minimum, together with bolometric corrections, so that the ratio of maximum to minimum total radiation is known, (b) spectra at maximum and minimum from which corresponding temperatures can be found, (c) accurate radial velocities throughout the cycle.

From the relative radiation and the temperatures at maximum and minimum, Stefan's law gives the *ratio* of radii R_{max}/R_{min}.[1] We can also calculate $R_{max} - R_{min}$ from the variation of radial velocity with time (fig. 40). We can draw a line which cuts the velocity-curve so that the two shaded areas are equal. The velocity defined by this line is the radial velocity of the star relative to the observer while the two areas (velocity × time) are equal to the total distance travelled upward or downward by the atmosphere in half the duration of a pulsation. This is the difference in radius between maximum and minimum phase. Knowing both $R_{max} - R_{min}$ and R_{max}/R_{min} we calculate R_{max} and R_{min} separately. We now have all the data needed to calculate the absolute magnitude, and hence the distance of a Cepheid variable.

When first applied this method yielded luminosities and distances that appeared to be too great. Doubts were felt about some assumptions underlying the argument; in particular, the velocity-curve refers to the atmospheric level where the absorption lines are formed, while the changes in brightness and temperature refer to truly photospheric levels which are probably lower. Moreover, the velocity-curves of Cepheids disagree in phase by a quarter of a period with the simplest predictions of the pulsation model, according to which maximum velocity of approach should occur before instead of at maximum light.

However, it now appears that pulsation parallaxes do after all give roughly the right answer, while the statistical parallaxes more commonly used were unreliable owing to the smallness of the proper motions.[2]

---

[1] $R^2_{max}/R^2_{min} = L_{max} \cdot T^4_{min}/L_{min} \cdot T^4_{max}$ where L is the luminosity.

[2] In 1952 Baade found from observations in the Andromeda nebula that the zero-point of the Period-Luminosity law needed correction by about $-1.5m$, i.e. that Cepheids with periods of, say, 10 days were $1.5m$ brighter than hitherto supposed. Immediate support to this correction was given by the discovery at the Radcliffe Observatory of RR

Even when the absolute magnitude of a Cepheid is known, we are still left with the problem of measuring the dimming effect of interstellar dust before the distance can be determined. The true colours of Cepheids, which are needed to measure this dimming, are imperfectly known, and until this problem is solved the distances of Cepheids will remain poorly determined.

Calcium emission as a distance indicator. A most remarkable empirical method of establishing distances of late-type stars has been developed recently by O. C. Wilson. Within the strong H and K absorption lines in the Sun we find two weak emission humps. These 'reversals' probably arise in the chromosphere, and are very strong in the region of sunspots.

Similar reversals can be observed, with high dispersion, in stars of types G to M. In dwarfs a narrow single emission is often found superposed on the absorption core; in supergiants much wider emission is cut in two by central absorption (fig. 45). Wilson finds a linear relationship between the total width of emission (indicated by arrows in the figure) and the luminosity. This relationship is not yet fully explained but it probably indicates systematically greater turbulence in the chromospheres of supergiants than in giants and dwarfs. From a practical point of view the emission width can be easily measured and from it the luminosity and hence the distance can be derived. Unfortunately the method can only be applied to bright stars; even with the 200-inch telescope it is difficult to push the observations to stars below naked-eye

Lyrae variables in the Magellanic Clouds about $1\cdot5m$ fainter than expected. The statistical parallaxes of RR Lyrae variables have not needed such a large correction as the Cepheids, since their proper motions are in general larger. The Period-Luminosity law is the subject of intensive current investigation, in its applicability to both Cepheids and RR Lyrae variables. In addition to residual doubts about the zero-point, it is suspected that there is not an entirely unique relation between Luminosity and Period.

brightness. However, the method promises to have important applications to supergiant stars whose distances are least well known.

Conclusions. We have considered in turn some of the methods of determining stellar distances. It must be recognized that there are still many weaknesses and it is an urgent matter to remove inaccuracies with improved techniques.

We know that a star whose spectrum has been classified

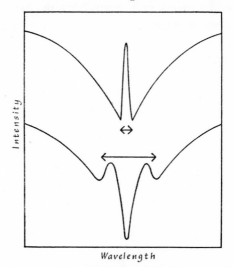

FIG. 45. Schematic profiles of Ca II line in late-type dwarfs (above) and supergiants (below).

accurately, say in the MK system (see p. 67), has a certain luminosity – with a considerable inaccuracy. The location of the brightest stars in fig. 14 (p. 64) is based mainly on the latest calibration of the MK system. The reason why the points show a clustering tendency along straight lines in the upper part of the diagram is that the spectra have been 'pigeon-holed' in luminosity classes that are still rather coarse. A re-calibration of the MK system is in progress; the results are eagerly awaited because spectroscopic parallaxes are commonly used as a first indicator of distance.

A comparison of spectroscopic and trigonometrical parallaxes (undertaken in 1937) indicated that the probable error of a spectroscopic distance of a main sequence star is 25 per cent, while for supergiants it appeared to be as large as 52 per cent. It is unlikely that the errors for main sequence stars have been appreciably diminished in the intervening years, while for giants and supergiants the error may well have been underestimated.

Chapter 13

GALAXIES

Many of the difficulties described in the last chapter disappear when we observe a galaxy outside the Milky Way which is still close enough to be resolved into separate stars. Within the Milky Way it is very difficult to distinguish the wood from the trees. When a large telescope is turned on the two Magellanic Clouds or the Andromeda nebula we can see both wood and trees. In such systems we can safely treat *all* the stars as though they were at the same distance from us (just as with the open clusters formerly discussed); measures of apparent magnitudes can be turned immediately into absolute magnitudes once we know the distance. Measures of relative brightness of such diverse objects as the brightest stars, Cepheid variables, novae at maximum, open and globular clusters, etc., can be made without knowing the distance at all. This is the ideal method of establishing luminosities in the upper part of the Hertzsprung–Russell diagram; distances of luminous objects in the Milky Way can best be established by measuring the distances of the Magellanic Clouds and so finding absolute magnitudes of the corresponding objects in the Clouds. The Magellanic Clouds are at about one-tenth the distance of the Andromeda nebula but are inaccessible in the northern hemisphere where most of the large telescopes are concentrated. Consequently progress in this problem has been sadly delayed.

However, before considering our detailed knowledge of these relatively near systems, we must discuss what we know about external systems in general.

Forms of galaxies. Direct photographs show that galaxies can be grouped into well-defined classes according to appearance alone. In Hubble's classification there were four main groups – the spirals, the barred spirals, the ellipticals and the irregulars. The resolution of nearby spirals like the Andromeda nebula into stars with the 100-inch telescope, and in particular the recognition of Cepheid variables in them, proved beyond question that the spiral nebulae lie far beyond the confines of the Milky Way. Typical of the irregulars are the Magellanic Clouds, with little central condensation, although the Large Cloud has a pronounced main axis from the ends of which emerge some faint curved structure; thus the Large Cloud bears some resemblance to the barred spirals. It seems quite certain that the Milky Way has spiral structure, but recently a suggestion that it belongs to the barred spiral group has been entertained.

Spectral characteristics. The integrated spectra of galaxies obtained by placing the spectrograph slit across their brightest portions are continuous with recognizable absorption due to Ca II H and K, the hydrogen lines, etc. They are thus consistent with the hypothesis that the main body of light comes from numerous unresolved stars. The spectral type assigned according to usual criteria changes with wavelength, being earlier in the violet than in the yellow and red. This is a natural consequence of the early-type stars radiating more strongly at the shorter wavelengths. Morgan and Mayall recognize spectral classes that range from A or F to K among many galaxies, when one concentrates on criteria in the narrow band of wavelengths 3850 to 4100 A in the violet. The nuclei of many spirals and ellipticals seem to consist of K type giants; M giants must also be present because Ti O bands appear in the red (for instance in the nucleus of the Andromeda nebula).

Many spirals also show [O II] 3727 emission in their

spectra. This bright line must originate in interstellar space rather than in stellar atmospheres; its presence indicates that an appreciable mass of such spirals is in the form of gas at low pressure rather than of stars. This important discovery was delayed because at one time few astronomical spectrographs could penetrate the spectral region beyond 3900 A. [O II] 3727 emission is also found in about 15 per cent of ellipticals – a very much lower proportion than in the spirals.

The distribution of hydrogen emission nebulae is well shown on direct photographs taken through filters which practically isolate the red Hα line. In the Andromeda nebula Baade has found many such emission nebulae to be strung along the spiral arms like beads on a string. This was the first indication that high density of gas is directly associated with the spiral arms.

Gaseous emission and luminous early-type stars are dominant in the irregular nebulae like the Magellanic Clouds with little or no central condensation. Morgan finds such a close connection of spectral type with central condensation that he is able to infer spectral types (designated by small letters *a*, *f*, *g*, *k*) from the degree of condensation shown on direct photographs.

Red shifts of galaxies. The spectra of such faint objects as the external galaxies can naturally only be obtained at low dispersion. Nevertheless, for the purpose of studying radial velocities it has been found well worth the effort to secure spectra of the faintest nebulae with very low dispersion.

The reason for this lies in the well-known discovery by Hubble and Humason that the distant galaxies show red shifts in their spectra which increase directly with their distance. In the largest shift recorded up to 1959 (with the 200-inch telescope) the H and K lines of calcium, the most easily recognized feature in the spectrum, are shifted by as much as

800 A. This transforms their normal violet colour into blue-green. Interpreted as a radial velocity this shift implies that the nebula in question is running away from us at a speed of slightly over 60,000 km/sec.[1] There is nothing particularly egocentric in believing that all the galaxies are running away from *us*. The measures are made relative to us; spectroscopic observations made from any other galaxy would reveal just the same apparent general recession from that galaxy.

Whether these red shifts are in fact due to outward motions in an expanding universe or to some other cause still remains to be proved. So far as the optical velocities go the shift varies with wavelength according to the Doppler–Fizeau principle from ultra-violet to red (a range of nearly two to one in wave-length). There is some evidence that radio observations at 21 cm yield the same 'velocity' as the optical observations; this would imply agreement over a range in wavelength of nearly a million to one.

It is a matter of great significance that the 'velocity' comes out very closely the same from atomic lines as different as hydrogen, oxygen, neon, etc. One suggested explanation for the red shifts is that the atomic constants have changed during the long lapse of time (many millions of years) taken by the light to reach us from these galaxies. We measure the shift of the lines relative to a laboratory source; the interpretation of the measured shift in terms of velocity assumes that the atoms behave in our laboratories now exactly as they did in the external galaxies millions of years ago when the light started on its journey. But we know that if there has been a change it must have affected various species of atoms in the

[1] In 1960 this record was broken. The 200-inch telescope recorded a red shift corresponding to a speed of about 140,000 km/sec (46 per cent of the velocity of light) for a nebula which was identified with a radio source originally discovered by radio astronomers at Cambridge (England).

same way so that their red shifts mimic a shift due to velocity. The interpretation in terms of real velocities is perhaps more easily acceptable.

Distances of galaxies. Although it has been established that the red shifts increase linearly with distance, so far as the observations go, the actual value of the constant of proportionality (known as H, or the Hubble constant) is still far from certain. Hubble himself found the value 550 km/sec per megaparsec. Baade's revision of the distance scale (1952) immediately reduced this by a factor 2. Sandage (1958) pointed out further uncertainties in the distances of the most remote galaxies and is inclined to set the value as low as $H = 50$ to 100.

It may be pointed out that one of the chief factors in the 1958 revision was the discovery that certain objects classified by Hubble as the brightest stars in the Virgo cluster of galaxies were not stars at all but enormous diffuse nebulae, reduced to pin-points of light. The distinction could have been made easily had spectra been available. The great doubt that now exists concerning the true value of H is entirely a consequence of the difficulty of measuring extragalactic distances. The uncertainty in measuring the spectroscopic shifts is relatively trivial.

Even though the actual value of H is so uncertain, *relative* distances of galaxies can be measured to a surprising degree of accuracy simply from the measured red shifts. For instance a galaxy with measured velocity of 20,000 km/sec must be twice as distant as one with velocity 10,000 km/sec. This conclusion should be good to 4 per cent, since accurate velocities for the nearest galaxies show that the peculiar motions of galaxies are of the order of 300 km/sec. We are thus led to the paradoxical situation that, so long as the red shifts increase directly with distance, we can plot the galaxies in space (on some unknown scale) with greater accuracy than we can plot the stars beyond the Sun's immediate neighbourhood in our own Galaxy.

The rotation of spiral nebulae. It was discovered quite early that if the slit of a spectrograph were placed along the major axis of the nucleus of the Andromeda nebula the absorption lines in the spectrum were inclined. This proved conclusively that the system was rotating. Since the lines were straight so far as they could be traced, the angular velocity is constant out to this distance. In other words the nucleus of the Andromeda nebula is rotating like a solid body.[1]

By contrast, the Milky Way near the Sun is rotating differentially as we have seen, with the outer parts rotating slower than the inner parts. This is to be expected if the greater part of the mass of the Milky Way is concentrated in its inner parts, far from the Sun.

It has been possible to trace the rotation of the Andromeda nebula and some other spirals much further from the nucleus through spectroscopic observation of knots of emission nebulosity or of the [O II] 3727 emission line due to the interstellar gas. As usual, such emission nebulae can be observed much more easily than individual stars whose light is weakened in the spectroscope by being spread into a continuum. By such means it has been possible to observe differential rotation in the outer parts of the spiral nebula M33. In the Andromeda nebula, the rotational velocity appears to remain remarkably constant in the outer parts.

The study of the variation in rotational velocity with dis-

[1] This statement refers to the main body of the nuclear regions (about $0°·1$ across). A very recent observation (1960) with the new 120-inch reflector of the Lick Observatory using an image tube converter at the coudé focus showed that the star-like nucleus of the Andromeda nebula (only about $0°·001$ across) is rotating with astonishing speed. One revolution must be completed in about half a million years as compared with about 20 million years for the main body of the nucleus hitherto studied.

tance from the centre of a nebula is important because it gives us some idea of the distribution of mass within the nebula. The constant velocity in the outer parts of the Andromeda nebula suggests that there is still a considerable mass of this galaxy which lies outside the limits of photographs.

It would be of great interest to study the detailed law of rotation of barred spirals because as yet we do not understand why some spirals should exhibit such strongly developed central bars. The meagre information available does not show

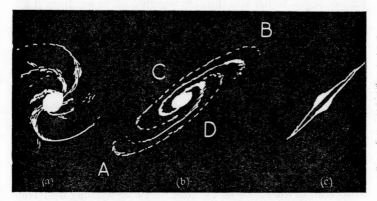

FIG. 46. The sense of rotation of spiral nebulae.

marked difference between the barred and the ordinary spirals in their rotation.

Spiral arms and the direction of rotation. The spiral nebulae are highly flattened systems, like the Milky Way. Those that are seen fully open (fig. 46a) show no effect of rotation in radial velocities because the motions are perpendicular to the line of sight.[1] Those that are seen edge-on (fig. 46c) show the maximum rotational effect in the spectroscope, but it is just these that fail to show spiral arms.

[1] The distances are far too great for proper motions across the line of sight to be discerned.

If we want to establish whether the rotation is in the sense of winding up or unwinding the spiral arms, we have to examine a spiral whose plane is inclined at a suitable intermediate angle (fig. 46b). Here the spiral pattern is seen sufficiently open to recognize the direction of winding, and at the same time there is still a sufficiently great difference in radial velocity of the opposite sides A and B to detect rotation.

Suppose that the spectroscope tells us that the side A is approaching and that side B is receding from us. We still cannot say whether the spiral is winding or unwinding. It all depends on whether side C or D, at ends of the minor axis, is nearer to us. If C is the nearer the spiral is unwinding; if D is nearer it is winding up. The spectroscope cannot help us to resolve the ambiguity. Direct photographs however do frequently show bands of absorbing dust which indicate which is the nearer side. Some fifteen spirals are known in which the orientation can be determined in this way with a fair degree of certainty and in which at the same time it is possible to trace the winding of the spiral arms and to measure the rotation. All cases seem to favour the view that the spiral arms trail in the rotation, i.e. that they are 'winding up'. This also seems to be the case with the Milky Way, although the radio observations suggest remarkably circular arms of small spiralling angle.

Theoretically the spiral arms pose a difficult problem which has not yet been solved. Radial velocities have shown unambiguously the differential rotation of the Milky Way near the Sun. A spiral arm subject to such differential rotation could not survive one or two revolutions without being torn apart and losing its identity. The Sun takes about 200 million years to complete a revolution in the Milky Way; and at this rate ought to have made some 30 revolutions during its existence. It is therefore suspected that the spiral arms may be extremely ephemeral in character; stars that are 'born' within them may fade into insignificance as the arms are sheared apart by differential rotation. New arms may be continually developed to replace the old. The role of interstellar gas and dust is probably of great importance in the development of spiral arms. But as far as the gas is concerned, we must not forget that the interstellar calcium and sodium gas shares in the differential rotation exhibited by the stars.

Stars in external galaxies. Although individual stars, e.g. novae, Cepheid variables, etc., have been extensively studied in nearby spirals our knowledge of their spectra is almost non-existent. Low-dispersion spectra of a few of the brightest stars in the Andromeda nebula have shown but few recognizable features. Some of these stars vary irregularly, a useful indication that they are isolated stars rather than unresolved clusters.

Detailed spectroscopic knowledge of stars outside the Milky Way is essentially restricted to the two Magellanic Clouds and has only recently become available with the establishment of 74-inch telescopes at the Radcliffe and Mt Stromlo Observatories.

The brightest stars in both Clouds are of about 10th apparent magnitude. In the Henry Draper Extension Catalogue some 200 stars are classified as B or as peculiar emission objects (including a considerable number of Wolf-Rayet stars). Subsequent slit spectra taken at the Radcliffe Observatory have shown that nearly every one of these 'B' stars have the radial velocity (+270 km/sec with regional variations) of the Large Cloud and also have very sharp lines characteristic of supergiants. There can be no doubt that these stars really belong to the Large Cloud. Their spectra have not revealed any *general* peculiarities which could be attributed, say, to differences in composition of the bulk of the matter forming the Cloud and our Milky Way.

The HR diagram of some of these brightest members of

the Clouds is shown in fig. 47. The two Clouds are at much the same distance, and apparent magnitudes can therefore be used in the combined diagram. The absolute magnitudes, based on a distance modulus of 19·2, appear on the right of the diagram.

The brightest star known in the Large Cloud, HD 33579, emits about a million times as much energy as the Sun. At times this may be exceeded by the variable star S Doradus.

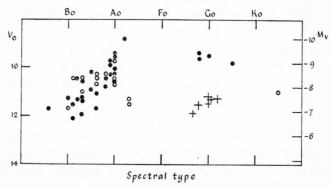

FIG. 47. HR diagram of the brightest stars in the Magellanic Clouds.
Filled circles: Large Cloud
Open circles: Small Cloud
Crosses:　bright Cepheids (both Clouds)
The ordinate on the left is V_0 the apparent magnitude, corrected for absorption; on the right appears the absolute magnitude.

Such stars are of type A. Their earlier classification as B was probably due to the exceedingly narrow hydrogen lines, far narrower than the familiar A stars of the Milky Way. In the HR diagram in fig. 47 there appears to be a band of stars stretching down to the left from the A type stars, so that for instance one does not meet stars of type O brighter than about 12·0 magnitude. It must be remembered that when proceeding from type A to O an increasingly large proportion of a star's radiation lies in the unobservable ultra-violet. *Bolo-*

metrically the total radiation from these stars of type A to O is probably much the same. These excessively luminous stars probably have masses of the order of 100 times that of the Sun. Stars more massive than this could not hold themselves together. On the right of fig. 47 there are a few red stars which must be among the largest stars known, with diameters about 1000 or 2000 times that of the Sun.

Some of the stars, including S Doradus when faint, show bright lines of [Fe II] in their spectra. When this occurs the total [Fe II] radiation must exceed the total energy output of the Sun. This characteristic recalls the spectrum of the ultra-slow nova η Carinae, a considerable proportion of whose radiation arises in a surrounding halo. One is thus led to question whether these exceptionally luminous objects in the Magellanic Clouds are true 'stars' in the ordinary sense of the word. The [Fe II] radiation probably arises in a vast low-excitation corona, perhaps resembling the solar corona.

Spectra of some of these Cloud stars show a double K line, one showing the radial velocity of the Cloud, the other, weaker, component having a small velocity. The weaker component must be due to interstellar calcium *in the Galaxy*. The stronger, high-velocity, component is usually to be attributed to the stellar atmosphere. In a few cases, however (particularly in Wolf-Rayet stars of high temperature), we can be sure that the line arises from interstellar calcium in the *Cloud*. Emission nebulae are very numerous in the Large Cloud and are not uncommon in the Small Cloud. Thus the presence of such Cloud interstellar lines is not surprising. Further, radio observations record the H 21 cm line coming from both Clouds; indeed, the interstellar hydrogen detected by radio telescopes is spread over large areas of the sky outside the boundaries of the Clouds shown on optical photographs.

Radial velocities within the Magellanic Clouds. Emission nebulae in the Clouds were studied spectroscopically by

N

observers of the Lick Southern Station. They found radial velocities of +276 and +168 km/sec for the Large and Small Cloud respectively.

These large velocities of recession are to a great extent due to the fact that the Sun is being carried away from the direction of the Clouds (particularly the Large Cloud) by the rotation of the Milky Way. It was noticed that the velocities of the nebulae varied across the Large Cloud in such a way that the Cloud might be rotating. It is now known from both optical and radio (21 cm) velocities that the Large Cloud is rotating.

Prosecution of observing programmes to determine velocities in various parts of the two Clouds will eventually show how the mass is distributed through each system, just as in the rotation of spiral nebulae. In addition to the systematic trends in the velocities across the Clouds due to their rotation, there are random motions. Accurate measures of such random motions can be used to measure the total mass of a system. Preliminary estimates of the masses of the Clouds made from the random motions suggest that they contain only a few per cent of the mass of our own Galaxy.

The Small Cloud appears to have a surprisingly large proportion of its mass in the form of neutral hydrogen, as judged by the strength of its 21 cm radiation. A considerable proportion of this radiation originates in a 'bulge' which points towards the Large Cloud. This bulge, although not very prominent in optical radiation, was originally discovered on direct photographs. It is likely that it arises as a consequence of tidal attraction by the Large Cloud.

A vast number of spectroscopic problems in both Clouds await investigation. Spectral classification of stars of apparent magnitude 15 or 16 is urgently required for comparison with galactic stars. At this apparent magnitude in the Clouds we reach an absolute magnitude of −4 or − 3; this is still rather high in the HR diagram among the supergiants and giants, where the luminosities of galactic stars are still very uncertain. Spectroscopic studies of special objects, the Cepheid variables, novae, Wolf-Rayet stars and other peculiar objects also have high priority. Both Clouds contain a large number of clusters, apparently globular in form, but in some cases differing from the globular clusters of our Galaxy in containing bright blue stars. Other globular clusters in the Clouds are normal in containing RR Lyrae variables. Spectra of both types of clusters deserve examination to determine their physical and dynamical properties.

A small beginning on such problems has been made, and the coming decades will certainly witness a very great expansion of spectroscopic research on the Magellanic Clouds.

Chapter 14

WIDTHS OF SPECTRUM LINES

Examined with high power the absorption lines in stellar spectra have a definite width. This width arises partly from the properties of the atoms responsible for the absorption line and partly from the properties of the stellar atmosphere.

We have frequently had occasion to refer to diagrams in which the energy levels of an atom are drawn as horizontal

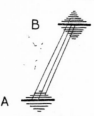

FIG. 48. The widths of energy levels contribute to the widths of absorption lines.

lines as though the atom contained a perfectly precise amount of energy in each level. The line corresponding to a transition between two such perfectly sharp levels would be perfectly sharp. The actual situation is better illustrated in fig. 48 where the two levels A and B have a certain width. The atom in state A or B is most likely to contain an amount of energy corresponding to the long heavy line; but it is also possible for the atom to contain slightly more or less than this average energy. We may speak of the states A and B being composed of a continuous set of sub-levels. The existence of such sub-levels means that, as a result of all the possible transitions between them, the absorption line A–B has a certain finite width whose profile may have some such shape as that shown in fig. 49a. The deep core of the profile corresponds in wavelength to the commonest transition, between the two heavy lines of fig. 48.

196

The 'wings' correspond to the rarer transitions between the outer sub-levels.

The dashed line indicates where the continuum would lie but for the presence of the absorption line. Consider a rectangular profile as in fig. 49*b* with height equal to the continuum and with area equal to that subtracted by the absorption line from the continuum in fig. 48*a*. The width $\Delta\lambda$ of the rectangle is called the *equivalent width* of the absorption line.

Measurement of profiles and equivalent widths. When the spectrum line is sufficiently wide and the spectroscopic resolution is sufficiently great it becomes possible to measure the profile or shape of the absorption line directly. This has been

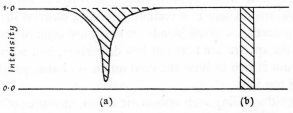

FIG. 49. The equivalent width of an absorption line.

done, by photographic and photo-electric photometry, for the stronger lines in the solar spectrum and for the very wide Balmer lines of hydrogen in stellar spectra.

The finite resolution of any spectroscope must broaden an infinitely sharp line into some definite shape characteristic of the instrument. It is possible to correct for this 'instrumental profile' and so obtain the true profile from that observed. However, most stellar spectra are taken with too low resolution for this refined study. Instead, many measures of equivalent width have been made; theoretically we expect the measured equivalent width to be *unchanged* by the imperfect resolution of the spectroscope. In other words, the equivalent width should be independent of the spectroscope used to observe it, although the profile will be markedly dependent on the instrumental resolution.

In practice, it is often found that measures of equivalent width made with small dispersion are too large. This practical problem has been the subject of considerable investigation by workers in different countries using entirely different instruments.

It is an unfortunate fact that large systematic errors in equivalent widths measured at different observatories do occur, in some cases running up as great as 25 per cent. The two most potent sources of error in such measures are (a) drawing in the continuum, and (b) proper allowance for blending lines which appear within the wings of the line to be measured. There is a certain subjective element in both these procedures. Weak blends are easily lost sight of entirely when the spectra are taken at low dispersion; and when the spectrum is rich in lines the continuum is almost inevitably drawn too low.

Notwithstanding such systematic errors, measures of equivalent width represent an advance in objectivity on numerical estimates by eye.

The curve of growth. Suppose that we devise a controlled laboratory experiment in which we measure the equivalent widths of absorption lines produced by columns of gas with known concentrations of atoms. We want to know how the equivalent width is related to the number of atoms N (per cm^2) in each absorbing column. If we plot the equivalent width against N (usually on a logarithmic scale) we obtain what is known as a *curve of growth*. It might be expected that W might increase directly with N and give a linear curve of growth, but this only happens in special circumstances. In general we find a curve whose shape depends on a number of physical factors. There are many reasons why the lines in stellar spectra have a definite width, but let us first consider the natural broadening which originates in the finite widths of the energy levels in fig. 48.

Natural broadening. The width of any level depends directly on the amount of time spent by the atom in that level. The quicker the atom leaves the level by a spontaneous downward transition, the broader will be the level. Atoms spend by far the greater part of their lives in the lowest level. Consequently the lowest level is the only one that can be regarded as almost perfectly sharp. Among the higher levels those that are metastable will always be sharper than those that are not.

With a transition between any two levels is associated a constant, the natural damping constant γ, which is a simple func-

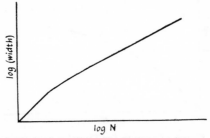

FIG. 50. Curve of growth for natural broadening alone.

tion of the life-times of the two levels. This damping constant controls the equivalent width of a line when great numbers of absorbing atoms are present.

When natural broadening alone is to be considered, the curve of growth takes the form illustrated in fig. 50. At low intensities the width is directly proportional to the number of atoms. As N increases the absorption line becomes saturated in the centre, and wings, due to natural damping, develop. The rate of growth becomes smaller; in the upper straight branch the width is proportional to $\sqrt{N\gamma}$. The actual position of this 'damping branch' depends on the value of the damping constant.

The natural damping is an inherent property of the atom. External causes, like near-collisions with other atoms, may perturb the atom to such an extent that any particular level is broadened still further. The Stark effect on the Balmer series of hydrogen is an extreme example of such broadening in excess of the natural broadening.

Doppler broadening. The second powerful source of broadening lies in the random motions of atoms whereby the Doppler effect causes them to absorb wavelengths away from the centre of the line. This smearing effect takes a very different form from that due to natural broadening. After satura-

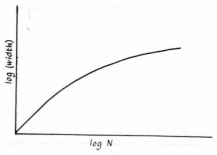

FIG. 51. Curve of growth for Doppler broadening alone.

tion the line has a bell-shaped form. Owing to the rarity of atoms with very high velocities the absorption is weak outside the wide core.

The curve of growth for Doppler broadening alone is shown in fig. 51. Again at low intensities the width increases directly with the number of atoms.

It must be noted that the role played by Doppler broadening is greater the higher the temperature, since the mean speed of the atoms is then increased. Moreover, at any given temperature it is greater for light atoms like H or He than for heavy atoms (Ca or Fe). For instance at the temperature of the solar atmosphere (5740° K) the Doppler width of the Hα line is 0·36 A; for a heavy atom like Fe the width is only 0·05 A (at the same wavelength as Hα).

Curve of growth for combined natural and Doppler broadening. Theoretical curves of growth for combined natural and Doppler broadening appear in fig. 52. These are shown for two values of the damping constant and for two values of the Doppler width (which may arise from different values of the temperature or atomic mass or other causes).

The only part of the curve of growth which is independent

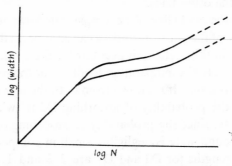

FIG. 52. Curve of growth for combined natural and Doppler broadening. The height of the flat intermediate branch depends on the Doppler width; the height of the right-hand branch depends on the damping constant.

of the two parameters, natural damping and Doppler broadening, is the left-hand branch, i.e. that involving the weakest lines. Owing to this circumstance the weakest lines are now recognized as the best indicators of abundance of the various elements in stellar atmospheres and are receiving increasing attention, particularly in the solar spectrum.[1] Unfortunately, in stellar spectra it is rare that the spectroscopic resolution is adequate for the accurate study of such faint lines.

Comparison of theory and observation. Although of course

[1] However, faint lines that are formed very *deep* in a stellar atmosphere can behave like strong lines as indicators of abundance.

we cannot vary the number of atoms in a stellar atmosphere as we can in the laboratory, we can build up a curve of growth for a stellar spectrum with the help of multiplets, and of ionization theory. In such a curve the equivalent width is plotted against the effective number of atoms in a state to absorb the line in question, $N \times f$, where N is the fraction of atoms in the lower level of the absorption line, and f, the *oscillator strength*, is a measure of the probability that an atom in that level will absorb the one particular line in preference to all the other lines.

Consider the Na D lines for example. The lower level is the ground state of the Na atom and we can assume all the neutral atoms to be in this state, or if necessary make a small correction according to the temperature to allow for the small number in excited states. It is known from both theory and observation that the probability of absorbing D2 is twice that of absorbing D1; since the probability of absorbing other lines from the ground state is negligibly small in comparison, the oscillator strengths for D2 and D1 are 2/3 and 1/3 respectively. The observed equivalent widths of D2 and D1 then give us a small section of the curve of growth, with a base-line (in Nf) of two to one.

A much larger base-line is given by some Fe multiplets within which the various lines may have oscillator strengths differing by a factor as large as 100. The base-line may be extended as far as we please by determining in the laboratory relative oscillator strengths of strong and weak multiplets.

Curves of growth in stellar spectra have been thus constructed in which the range of Nf exceeds 1000. In the solar spectrum such weak lines can be observed that the range is about 100,000. Such curves of growth do indeed show the form of fig. 52, although few lines are strong enough to lie on the upper asymptote of the curve. The majority of observed lines lie on the flat intermediate portion.

Turbulence. The flat Doppler branch of the curve is particularly prominent in the spectra of certain stars. The Doppler width deduced (up to 67 km/sec) was in many cases much larger than could be attributed to thermal motion of the atoms at the surface temperatures of the stars concerned.

A rational way out of this difficulty was to postulate that the excessive Doppler width was due not to thermal motions of the atoms but to motions of large clouds in the stellar atmosphere (perhaps rather like the solar granulation). It is important to note that the light, in escaping from the star, must pass through a number of these so-called turbulent elements. If the turbulent elements are all ranged side by side (as for instance in the ordered motion of upward and downward convection currents) and not superposed, then the equivalent width in the spectrum of each will be the same; the *profile* of the integrated spectrum from all such elements will be smeared out and broadened, but the equivalent width will be unchanged – a smearing effect just like that of an imperfectly resolving spectroscope. If however the turbulent elements are superposed, then the formation of the absorption line in the stellar atmosphere will take place as if the Doppler width were increased (whether due to motions of atoms or turbulent clouds).

It is possible to check this hypothesis to some extent by observing directly the shapes of the line-profiles with high dispersion. A Doppler width can be deduced directly from the profiles, or more indirectly from the curve of growth. In the few stars investigated in both ways it has usually been found that the turbulent velocity derived from the profiles is larger than that derived from the curve of growth. Much work remains to be done to improve our understanding of the physical conditions in stellar atmospheres, and more particularly the factors governing the intensities and profiles of absorption lines.

Stark effect. The broadening of lines by Stark effect in stellar atmospheres is essentially confined to the lightest elements hydrogen and helium. The very wide wings of hydrogen among B type dwarfs are due to Stark effect apparently produced by interatomic fields. The narrower lines in giants and supergiants are easily understood in terms of the lower pressures in these atmospheres which will consequently greatly weaken such electric fields. It is of interest to note in passing that certain *forbidden* lines of helium have been observed as absorption lines in B type dwarfs but not giants or supergiants. These forbidden transitions have been observed to occur in the laboratory in the presence of strong electric fields.

It is possible to estimate the electron pressure in a stellar atmosphere in whose spectrum the hydrogen lines are broadened by Stark effect. As we proceed along the Balmer series towards the ultra-violet there comes a point (even with high resolution) when the lines can no longer be separately distinguished. This occurs earlier in the series in spectra strongly affected by Stark effect. A simple formula gives the electron pressure as a function of the number of the last member of the Balmer series that can be detected.[1]

Axial rotation. We have seen in Chapter 6 that some stars have very broad shallow lines attributed to rapid rotation. Consider for instance a rotating star (with axis lying in the plane of the sky) whose equatorial velocity is 200 km/sec. The Hγ line arising from approaching and receding ends of the equator will be displaced by 3 A to violet and red of the Hγ line from the centre of the star's disk. Most of the light

---

[1] If N_e is the concentration of electrons per cm^3, and n_m is the number of the last resolved member of the Balmer series

$$\log N_e = 23 \cdot 06 - 7 \cdot 5 \log n_m$$

See Inglis and Teller, *Ap. J.* **90**, 439, 1939, and F. L. Mohler, *Ap. J.* **90**, 429, 1939.

we observe comes from the centre of the disk since we must expect all stars to be darkened to the limb like the Sun (p. 100). We cannot distinguish light from different parts of the disk, but the integrated effect will be a broadened line with a width somewhat less than 6 A.

Axial rotation of course affects lines of all elements similarly but varies with wavelength according to the Doppler–Fizeau principle. In this respect it can be distinguished from the Stark effect, dominantly shown by hydrogen and helium. Actual speeds of rotation can be measured in eclipsing binaries (p. 124). In single stars, an analysis of the profile of a line (like Mg II 4481) can yield the velocity of rotation *in the line of sight*, but without knowing where the axis of rotation lies we cannot measure the true equatorial velocity of rotation. Statistically, however, if we assume that the axes of rotation are distributed at random in space, one can deduce some interesting correlations of rotation with other physical properties.

We know that rapid rotation occurs most commonly among stars of type O to early F, and that there is a very sharp drop in rotation among stars of type F5 and later.

Many B type stars with wide lines show bright hydrogen lines. For such stars there is a correlation between the widths of the absorption lines and of the hydrogen emission. This correlation is probably due to varying inclinations of the rotational axis; stars with the narrowest absorption and emission lines have their axes of rotation pointing towards us. Rapid rotation in itself is likely to throw out gas centrifugally into equatorial rings in which an emission spectrum can originate.

Magnetic stars. The most recently discovered contributor to the width of stellar lines is Zeeman effect. Our knowledge of magnetic fields in stars rests almost entirely on the observations of Zeeman effect by H. W. Babcock with the coudé spectrographs of the 200-inch and 100-inch telescopes. Just as in Hale's discovery of magnetic fields in sunspots, Babcock used an analyser to suppress one or the other of the outer polarized portions of the Zeeman pattern; a relative shift (varying in a predictable manner from line to line) is proof of the presence of a magnetic field. The measured shift in the apparatus used is a few microns for a field of 1000 gauss.

The first star in which a magnetic field was discovered (1947) was the peculiar A type star 78 Virginis. The peculiarity lies in strong and sharp lines of strontium, chromium and europium. Many other A stars are known with peculiarly strong lines of such elements, or of manganese, silicon, etc. Magnetic fields are almost invariably detected in such 'metallic' A stars, provided the lines are sharp enough.

Rotational broadening is very common among the A type stars. It is probable that these sharp-line A stars with magnetic fields are also rotating, but that the rotation does not blur the spectra because the axis of rotation lies more or less along the line of sight. These are 'pole-on' stars.

A puzzling feature of these magnetic stars is that in virtually all cases adequately observed the magnetic field varies and sometimes even changes sign. 53 Camelopardus, with the highest field yet observed, varies between −4350 and +3700 gauss.[1] The spectra of the magnetic stars also vary frequently. In α^2 Canum Venaticorum, for instance, the lines of europium and chromium vary oppositely in phase. Neutral and ionized chromium vary together in a manner that defies explanation in terms of ionization theory.

Two models have been considered. In one, the star's surface oscillates and carries the lines of force with it at varying angles to the line of sight. This model fits those stars where the magnetic field and the spectrum both vary with the same period. However, RR Lyrae, the type-star of pulsating short-period

[1] In 1960 Babcock reported that the star HD 215441 had shown a maximum magnetic field of 34,400 gauss on four consecutive nights.

variables, with a very regular light-variation in a period of 0·56683735 days, shows magnetic variations in which it has been impossible to find any regular period.

In the second model (the 'oblique rotator') the magnetic axis does not coincide with the axis of rotation. The magnetic field is taken to be constant, but we view different parts of it at different phases of rotation.

Neither model has been fully accepted, and we know nothing as yet of the origin of these strong magnetic fields, although it seems likely to be connected in some way with rapid rotation.

The importance of the subject is clear in that magnetic fields have been detected in some objects other than the peculiar A type stars; in RR Lyrae (but not as yet in any classical Cepheid variable[1]), in the long period variable R Geminorum of S type, and in several peculiar M type giants with emission lines (including the eclipsing variable VV Cephei).

Negative results have been found for such stars as Sirius (A0 dwarf), Betelgeuse (M supergiant), 61 Cygni (K6 dwarf), Pleione (shell star in the Pleiades). The minimum field detectable in sharp-line stars can be less than 50 gauss.

The widening of lines due to the largest fields found must have an appreciable effect on measures of equivalent width. However, there is no reason to fear that 'magnetic broadening' of lines is an important factor in determining the widths of lines in an average star. Magnetic broadening is appreciable in the spectra of solar sunspots but not in integrated sunlight such as would be observed from another star.

Hyperfine structure. Some lines observed with very high resolution in the laboratory are found to have complicated multiple structure. This *hyperfine structure* arises in two distinct ways from properties of the atomic nucleus. Hitherto

[1] A magnetic field is regarded as probably present in the Cepheid FF Aquilae.

the positive electrical charge on the nucleus has been the sole factor determining the energy levels with which we have been concerned.

One type of hyperfine structure arises from the spin-energy of the nucleus and its interaction with the surrounding electrons. This is intrinsic to the atom, independent of all external circumstances. It appears that this type of hyperfine structure contributes appreciably to the widths of certain lines in the solar spectrum. The best example is provided by some lines of manganese whose observed widths, interpreted as Doppler broadening, correspond to 5·5 km/sec; this is more than three times the width due to true Doppler broadening in the solar atmosphere.

The second way in which the nucleus can contribute to the widths of lines is through the presence of different isotopes. Each isotope has the same pattern of lines, but there is a minute shift in wavelength from one isotope to another; the wavelength is determined by the ratio of mass: nucleus/electron, but the shift is very small because the nucleus is always overwhelmingly heavier than the electron. Deuterium being twice as heavy as ordinary hydrogen has a line corresponding to Hα shifted by as much as 1·79 A – an exceptionally large isotopic shift. Abundant deuterium could therefore produce an appreciable degree of broadening, but this has not in fact been observed.

The determination of abundances of various isotopes will be considered in the next chapter. The problem is approached more efficiently, as will be seen, in studying molecular bands than atomic lines.

Chapter 15

THE COMPOSITION OF
THE UNIVERSE

Ever since the spectroscope first allowed us to probe stellar atmospheres and to detect the presence of familiar terrestrial atoms in them, it has been the astrophysicists' ambition to *measure* and compare abundances of atomic species in different parts of the universe. Is the Sun composed of the same elements as the Earth, and in the same proportion? Are all stars the same in composition? Do the gaseous nebulae or the ocean of interstellar matter differ from the stars?

It is unfortunately still a far easier matter to detect the mere presence of any atomic species in a stellar atmosphere than to measure its abundance relative to another. The difficulties of measuring intensities of lines objectively (in bright stars) have largely been overcome with powerful modern spectroscopes, although there is still room for improvement. It is in the interpretation of observed equivalent widths in terms of abundances that most of the difficulty lies. Strangely enough, the missing factor is most commonly one that can be measured in the laboratory – that is the *oscillator strengths* of lines found in stellar spectra.

The Russell mixture. The ionization theory showed that the characteristic patterns of lines in the spectral sequence could be explained in terms of varying temperature in atmospheres with a *constant relative abundance of the elements* (p. 81). The result was necessarily a rough one, but it lent confidence

o

209

to the hypothesis that a detailed analysis of the Sun's atmosphere might give us the maximum information about the composition of an average star.

In a classical investigation (1929) H. N. Russell used visual estimates of lines from the Rowland Catalogue and found abundances of elements very similar to those which have been derived since by the much more refined methods of the curve of growth. The relative abundances found for the Sun in this analysis became known as the 'Russell mixture'. It had two especially important features.

One was that hydrogen is easily the most abundant element outnumbering all the other atoms put together. The other was that atoms of even atomic number are on the average about ten times more abundant than those of odd atomic number. The second result agreed with previous analyses of the composition of the Earth's crust and of meteorites. The abundance of solar hydrogen is certainly not repeated in the Earth's crust nor in meteorites. However, several arguments pointed simultaneously to the conclusion that extra-terrestrial hydrogen is by far the most abundant element in the universe.

The abundance of hydrogen. In the first place, Eddington's theory of stellar interiors (1924) predicted a luminosity for a star of given mass that was originally at variance with observation. The predicted luminosity was very sensitive to the mean molecular weight of stellar material. It so happens that in the heavily ionized conditions of stellar interiors the mean molecular weight will be nearly 2 for almost any mixture of the elements *except hydrogen*, which by itself would give a molecular weight of 0·5.[1] The predicted mass–luminosity rela-

[1] A star composed entirely of hydrogen may be assumed to have *m* neutral atoms (mass *H*) and *n* ions (also mass *H*) and *n* free electrons (of negligible mass.) The mean molecular weight is $(m + n)/(m + 2n)$. Except at the surface, hydrogen must be ionized within all stars; i.e. $m = 0$ and the mean molecular weight becomes 0·5.

For all the heavy elements, we must remember that Z free electrons

tion gave the correct result if hydrogen were taken to be superabundant, just as Russell found for the Sun from his analysis of its spectrum.

Secondly, the identification of ammonia and methane in the spectra of the major planets showed that hydrogen must be an abundant constituent in the atmospheres of these heavy planets. The relative lack of hydrogen in the Earth is easily understood; hydrogen as the lightest element will be the first to escape by evaporation into outer space. This escape proceeds rapidly from a light planet like the Earth. It must proceed still more rapidly from small bodies like meteorites.

Thirdly, Russell himself pointed out that the fogginess of the atmospheres of A type stars was due to the ionization of the abundant hydrogen. This fogginess prevents lines such as those of ionized iron becoming as intense as the ionization theory, in its simplest form, predicted.

Fourthly, the bright Balmer lines found in the spectra of diffuse nebulae (and in the much larger tracts of the Milky Way revealed by nebular spectrographs) were understood to indicate that the superabundance of hydrogen extended also to interstellar space. The elements calcium and sodium only happened to be recognized first in interstellar space through the chance circumstance of their resonance lines lying in the easily observable part of the spectrum.

We have noted on several occasions the unfortunate fact that the Balmer lines arise from excited levels with 10 volts excitation potential, while the resonance lines in the Lyman series lie in the far ultra-violet. In order to analyse the abundance of hydrogen from the Balmer lines (in absorption) we

will be released by an atom with atomic number Z, in the ionized conditions of stellar interiors. For instance, iron, with atomic weight 56 and atomic number 26, will release 26 electrons when fully stripped, so that within a hypothetical star composed entirely of iron the mean molecular weight would be $56/(26 + 1) = 2\cdot1$.

have to apply an enormous correction for the 10 volts excitation; moreover, Stark broadening controls the equivalent widths to such an extent that each Balmer line has to be treated as a special problem.

The same difficulty with regard to excitation occurs with all the important light elements – helium, carbon, nitrogen, oxygen and neon, none of whose resonance lines are observable. The relative abundance of these light elements to the metals in the Sun is still subject to some uncertainty.

The relative abundances of the light atoms and the metals found by various spectroscopic methods have been roughly but surprisingly confirmed in a very different field – that of cosmic rays. These rays are now understood to consist primarily of highly energetic particles (before they produce many secondary radiations in the Earth's atmosphere); and the striking feature is that the primary particles are mainly hydrogen atoms, followed in numbers by helium, oxygen, etc., and even iron, roughly in the same proportion as in the Russell mixture.

Comparison of stars, nebulae, Sun and Earth. Apart from the Sun, modern efforts to analyse relative abundances by the method of the curve of growth have been concentrated mainly on stars of type O, B, A and F. The stars of later type have spectra so crowded with lines that blending is a serious problem, and it is impracticable to measure a large range of intensities accurately.

The B stars are particularly suited to photometry of the spectrum with a well-defined continuum. These hot stars fail to show lines due to elements heavier than iron or nickel (and very few elements heavier than sulphur), but this is only a spectroscopic accident. The relative abundances of the light elements can be studied with great profit in them, although account must still be taken of Stark broadening of hydrogen and helium lines.

Similarly the gaseous and planetary nebulae show many bright lines (permitted and forbidden) from which the relative abundances of light elements may be derived. Here the permitted lines of hydrogen and helium are due to recapture of free electrons and the theoretical derivation of abundances is perhaps on safer grounds. Progress has been made too in the derivation of abundances from the forbidden lines; the intensities of these lines, excited by electron impact, depends on the relative probabilities of atoms in various states suffering collision with an electron.

In analysing the intensities of permitted lines in the nebulae it must be remembered that some lines are excited by Bowen's fluorescent mechanism (p. 138); the intensities will then be far more dependent on the closeness of coincidence in wavelength of the exciting line than on the abundance of the element of the question. In discussing abundances such selectively excited lines must clearly be avoided.

As a result of extensive analyses of spectra of the Sun, normal stars and nebulae, we reach the conclusion that as regards atomic constitution the spectroscope has not yet revealed any really outstanding differences (see table on following page).

Peculiar abundances. As a result of such comparisons the view strengthened that the Russell mixture (or its more refined counterpart) is a constant characteristic of most parts of the universe; the Earth and meteorites must be regarded as exceptional in their lack of the light elements.

However, many peculiar stars are known which suggest departures from the Russell mixture. These have been receiving increasing attention in recent years. Departures from a constant mixture are to be expected in *stellar interiors* because there the nuclear processes, known to be responsible for the production of stellar energy, will gradually exhaust certain atomic fuels after many millions of years and replace them with others.

COSMICAL ABUNDANCES

(The tabulated quantity is $\log_{10} N$, where N is the relative number of atoms. The data for Sun, stars and nebulae are adjusted so that $\log N = 12.00$ for hydrogen)

	Element	Earth's Crust	Meteorites	Sun	Early Stars	Planetary Nebulae
1	H	6·17	—	12·00	12·00	12·00
2	He	—	—	—	11·30	11·3
3	Li	3·57	3·40	0·83	—	—
6	C	4·49	—	8·28	8·36	—
7	N	3·58	—	8·15	8·52	8·4
8	O	7·53	—	8·68	9·01	8·8
10	Ne	—	—	—	9·02	8·0
11	Na	5·15	6·04	6·14	—	—
12	Mg	6·00	7·36	7·27	8·04	—
13	Al	6·54	6·38	6·06	6·69	—
14	Si	7·06	7·40	7·43	7·69	—
16	S	4·27	6·39	6·91	7·51	7·8
17	Cl	4·01	4·72	—	—	5·3
19	K	5·88	4·90	4·87	—	—
20	Ca	6·02	6·09	6·23	6·50	—
21	Sc	2·71	2·85	3·12	—	—
22	Ti	5·03	4·79	4·82	—	—
25	Mn	4·32	5·24	5·24	—	—
26	Fe	6·01	7·18	6·83	—	—
28	Ni	3·20	5·84	5·73	—	—

Courtesy M. G. J. Minnaert, *Month. Not. Roy. Ast. Soc.* **117**, 317, 1957, where the original tabulation includes data for all elements 1 to 30, as well as columns for the entire Earth and the mean for stars of Population I. (For description of stars of Populations I and II see p. 226.)

Carbon stars. The most easily recognized peculiarity of all, suspected for many years as due to anomalous composition, concerns the cool carbon stars of type N and R. The N stars with their strong C_2 and CN bands are so different from the M stars with their Ti O bands that Secchi placed them in his fourth class.

The distinction between the N and M stars can be easily understood if carbon is taken to be more abundant than oxygen in the N's, while the opposite is assumed for the M's. Most carbon and oxygen in cool stellar atmospheres will combine to form CO. The expected bands of CO lie in the unobservable ultra-violet. After formation of CO any residual oxygen will be taken up by other atoms to form molecular compounds like Ti O with high energy of dissociation. But if carbon outnumbers oxygen the oxygen compounds will be suppressed in favour of carbon compounds. Calculations based on ionization theory confirm this qualitative prediction.[1]

Carbon isotopes. We have already seen that various isotopes of one atom will give practically identical spectra, the minuteness of the shifts in wavelength being due to the large mass of the nucleus relative to the electron. However, when two atoms combine in a molecule the differences in wavelength of bandheads due to various isotopes become large, because now we are concerned with the relative mass of atom to atom instead of nucleus to electron. Carbon has three isotopes of mass 12, 13 and 14. A familiar band of C_2 at 4737 A is due entirely to $C^{12}.C^{12}$ (the isotope of mass 12 being far the commonest on Earth by a factor 90 : 1); but the corresponding band of $C^{12}.C^{13}$ is shifted to 4744 A, and can therefore easily be distinguished on stellar spectra of fairly low dispersion. This $C^{12}.C^{13}$ band is observed in R and N stars and the relative intensity allows one to estimate relative abundances of the isotopes of mass 12 and 13. It has been found that R and N stars can be divided into two groups according to the ratio $C^{12} : C^{13}$. In one group this ratio is about 3 and in the other

[1] Another interesting prediction from such calculations is that two molecules H_2 and H_2O ought to be very abundant in cool stellar atmospheres; the bands of H_2 are unsuitably placed, while with H_2O the difficulty is chiefly blending with terrestrial water vapour in the spectra. Neither molecule has yet been detected in stellar spectra.

it can be as high as 50 or more, like the ratio on Earth. In comets the ratio $C^{12} : C^{13}$ varies but is never near 3 as in some N stars. In interstellar space all that can be said from the faint molecular lines is that the ratio is greater than 5.

Another peculiarity of cool carbon stars is that the red resonance line of lithium has been found to be extraordinarily strong in three N type variables, WZ Cassiopeiae, WX Cygni and T Arae. A real excess of lithium is indicated in these stars, rather than an exceptionally low state of ionization. The observation is of importance in problems of nuclear sources of stellar energy, to be considered in the next chapter.

Other carbon stars. There is a suggestion of excessive carbon in some stars of earlier types than R and N. In the hottest stars we saw that the Wolf-Rayet stars seem to form two parallel sequences, one with strong carbon emission the other with strong nitrogen emission. The distinction is not entirely precise as WR stars combining C and N are known.

It is just possible that a continuous 'carbon sequence' of peculiar stars exists joining the hot Wolf-Rayet and the cool R and N stars. In a small group of stars of intermediate temperature molecular C_2 bands are strong, while CH is weak, as though there were a deficiency of hydrogen. This group contains R Coronae Borealis and other similar variables which suddenly fade to minimum light at unpredictable intervals, later returning slowly to normal brightness. In R Coronae Borealis exceptionally strong lines of C I confirm the suspicion that carbon is unusually abundant.

In another group, strong CH absorption is observed while the lines due to metals are weak. Stars with this spectroscopic peculiarity have high velocities. In another small group of 'barium stars', which seems to be associated with carbon stars, the lines of ionized barium are unusually strong.

Globular clusters. Spectra of globular clusters are usually known by observing the integrated light of the whole cluster, but in a few cases spectra of the brightest stars have been observed. Typical peculiarities are weakness of the CN band and of the metallic lines. Such stars cannot be classified according to ordinary criteria without running into inconsistencies. For instance, a spectral class assigned according to the strength of the hydrogen lines is likely to be later than one assigned according to the strength of the metal lines, perhaps by a whole spectral class; and a different class again will be found if the strength of CH is used. Some globular clusters are far more 'metal-weak' than others. According to some estimates the metal/hydrogen abundance may be smaller by a factor from 10 to 100 for such stars compared with the Sun.

It must be a highly significant fact that metal-weakness is also shown by a considerable number of isolated stars which, like the globular clusters, have large space velocities relative to the Sun. This strange correlation of physical and dynamical properties is being intensively studied at present.

The S stars. It will be recalled that this relatively rare type of cool star is characterized by bands of zirconium oxide. These stars have excited interest recently through the unexpected discovery of lines of the unstable element technetium in their spectra. Strong bands of lanthanum oxide have also been discovered in the infra-red.

White dwarfs. It has only been practicable to observe spectra of many white dwarfs recently with the 200-inch telescope. The peculiarities are so pronounced that it has not yet been possible to devise any satisfactorily comprehensive scheme of classification. This is very probably due to wider variations in the abundances of elements among the white dwarfs than in any other part of the HR diagram.

For many years it has been considered likely that white dwarfs represent the end-product of stellar evolution. Hydrogen, the chief source of stellar energy, is expected to be exhausted in their interiors. Although wide hydrogen lines were all that could be seen in the spectra of the earliest recognized white dwarfs, this is no evidence against hydrogen deficiency in the interior. The more recent studies have indeed shown examples where hydrogen does seem to be completely absent from the atmosphere.

Hydrogen-poor stars. Besides the white dwarfs there are a few isolated stars of greater luminosity in which weakness or absence of hydrogen lines point strongly to deficiency of hydrogen in the atmosphere. Among stars of type earlier than A (judged by the presence of helium) there are three outstanding instances, HD 124,448, 168,476, and 160,641; the first two are also remarkable in showing no lines due to oxygen either. Later types with very weak hydrogen lines are represented by v Sagittarii and HD 30,353.

Peculiar A stars. The classification of A stars is frequently difficult on account of peculiarities in certain lines. As much as 13 per cent of the stars classified as B8 to F0 have been found to show either strong silicon or strontium, or weak calcium.

Simple interpretation of these peculiarities in terms of anomalous abundances in stellar composition has become doubtful since the discovery of stellar magnetic fields. Ten per cent of the peculiar A stars show varying intensities of these lines, and in most cases a varying magnetic field has been found. It seems quite probable that there is a localization of elements on the star's surface, some being concentrated at the poles, others at the equator.

Metallic line stars. Some peculiar 'A' stars with strong metallic lines are now classified as F stars with weak metallic lines. Some are bright enough for a detailed study of the curve of growth. In τ Ursa Majoris, for instance, it appears that Ca, Sc, Ti, Zr are deficient, while Na, Sr, Zn are overabundant compared with the Sun. Greenstein noticed that the second ionization potentials of the 'deficient' elements all lay between 12 and 16 volts; it is possible that some mechanism might selectively ionize these elements so that doubts may be felt about interpreting the weakness of the lines in terms of peculiar abundances.

To conclude, the analysis of stellar spectra suggests that for the most part the atmospheres of stars are rather closely similar in composition. Even in the relatively rare cases of peculiar spectra it is difficult to prove how deep-seated or superficial is the peculiarity. However, the nuclear reactions that must be proceeding within the stars and providing the source of their energy will involve a secular change in the composition of stellar material. Great interest therefore attaches to the discovery of any spectroscopic peculiarity that may involve unusual composition, more especially when such a peculiarity extends to a recognizable *group* of stars, such as the carbon bands of R and N types or the weakness of metallic lines in many globular clusters and in stars with dynamical properties related to those of globular clusters. The study of anomalous abundances in stellar atmospheres is closely bound up with the theory of stellar evolution which is to be considered in the final chapter.

Chapter 16

STELLAR EVOLUTION AND
CURRENT PROBLEMS

The era of stellar spectroscopy may be taken as beginning in 1859 (by chance coinciding with the year of the publication of Darwin's *Origin of Species*). As soon as a sequence of physical types of stars became recognizable from their spectra it was natural that attempts would be made to fit them into some theory of evolution. A whole series of theories of stellar evolution have been proposed in turn and eventually abandoned. With the recognition during the last two decades of the chief nuclear sources of stellar energy, astrophysicists are now riding on the crest of a wave of optimism that we are at last in sight of the solution. We must confine ourselves here mainly to the spectroscopic contexts of the problem and refer the reader elsewhere for details of the current theory.

Ever since Aston's accurate measures showed that the mass of a helium atom is slightly less than four times that of the proton, it was realized that if four hydrogen atoms could somehow be fused together to form a single helium atom, then enough energy would be released to keep a star burning its hydrogen fuel for a long time compared with the geological age of the Earth. Two cycles are now recognized as performing this function in stellar interiors:[1]

(1) the proton–proton reaction, applicable to the Sun and cooler main sequence stars,

[1] For details see Appendix VI (p. 239).

220

(2) the carbon cycle, applicable to stars hotter than the Sun, in which carbon, nitrogen and oxygen act as catalysts in a series of reactions.

In either process, the fusion of four hydrogen atoms into one helium atom results in the conversion of a very small proportion (only 0·7 per cent) of the mass into radiant energy. If the Sun (with mass 2×10^{33} gm) consisted solely of hydrogen, it could burn into helium 'ash' at its present rate (10^{41} ergs/year) for as long as 10^{11} years and still preserve 99·3 per cent of its original mass. Nuclear processes can therefore cause stars to evolve for astronomical periods of time without appreciable loss of mass. Some astronomers however believe that the brighter stars evolve by ejecting considerable fractions of their total mass during their lives. Certainly in the upper part of the HR diagram there is some spectroscopic evidence that some stars (e.g. novae and P Cygni stars, etc.) are losing matter at their surfaces. In some binaries too there may be a continual loss of material from one component to the other. The part played by loss of (or gain of) mass in stellar evolution is still debated. But for ordinary stars like the Sun we are probably safe in ignoring it and assuming that during most of a star's life its mass remains essentially constant.

The degree of *mixing* of different layers in a star has a profound effect on the prediction of a star's evolutionary path. The observation that lithium is present in the Sun's atmosphere is strong evidence that the Sun is *not* well mixed, because lithium must disappear very rapidly in stellar interiors in the presence of neutrons. It is now accepted on theoretical grounds that only rapidly rotating stars can be subject to appreciable mixing. Consequently inhomogeneities must occur with hydrogen being gradually exhausted in the central cores.

This conclusion is disappointing to the spectroscopist who

hopes to analyse a star's composition by observing the spectrum of its outer skin in the atmosphere. However, there are a few stars mentioned in the last chapter with atmospheres apparently devoid of hydrogen, including some white dwarfs. It is difficult to avoid the conclusion that in these cases the hydrogen deficiency extends to the interior; on current theories these stars are extremely old, having exhausted their main fuel.

Carbon isotopes of mass 12, 13 and 14 all enter into the carbon cycle and when this cycle operates a ratio $C^{12} : C^{13} = 4\cdot3 \pm 1\cdot6$ is to be expected. This agrees with the observed ratio in the atmospheres of those carbon stars with strong C^{13}. It is possible that these stars are well mixed and that the ratios are the same at their surfaces as in their deep interiors.

Evolution of clusters. It is commonly believed that all stars within any one cluster were 'born' at approximately the same epoch, but that different clusters have very different ages ranging from a few million years to about 5×10^9 years. On this hypothesis the HR diagram of any cluster must be an important guide to the way in which stars evolve. We cannot of course hope to see stars evolving during a few decades, but star clusters give us snapshots of whole families of stars at different stages of their evolution.

A typical star cluster like the Pleiades has an HR diagram like that represented in fig. 53 by the curve $A'BC$. ABC represents the ordinary main sequence, and the cluster stars coincide with this over the branch BC, but the brightest stars lie above it, at A' for instance.

This phenomenon can be understood in that the brightest (and most massive) stars like A' are burning their hydrogen fuel far more lavishly than B or C and are consequently evolving more rapidly. When hydrogen consumption (in the deep interior) has reached a critical stage, a star at A moves away from the main sequence, becoming still brighter along the path AA'. In doing so its mass remains more or less constant; therefore while the star obeys the mass–luminosity relation while in the state A, it is too bright for the relation at A'. B, evolving more slowly than A, may be regarded as having just reached the critical stage, but not yet having started to move away from the main sequence. C, evolving still more slowly, will remain at its present position in the diagram for many millions of years before it also moves upwards on a

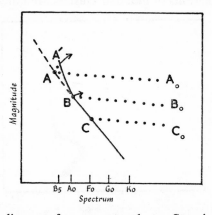

FIG. 53. HR diagram of an open star cluster. Stars in the cluster lie along the continuous curve $A'BC$. A' has evolved from the point A on the main sequence. B is near the end of its life on the main sequence and will evolve along the direction of the arrow. It is believed that stars reach the main sequence quickly via tracks A_0A, B_0B, C_0C.

similar path. Stars that were brighter and more massive than A, are considered to have evolved so rapidly that they have exhausted their fuel and are no longer visible (or perhaps to have moved across the diagram to the right to become red giants, in some unexplained way, as observed in some clusters). By fixing the critical point B where stars are just beginning to turn away from the main sequence, an estimate of a cluster's age may be made.

Little is known about the earliest stages of a star's evolution, but it is believed that they contract gravitationally along such tracks as A_0A, B_0B, C_0C. The T Tauri variables found commonly in clusters mixed with nebulosity are believed to represent this early stage.[1] The contraction can hardly continue for more than a few million years, so that stars in this phase of evolution must be far rarer than those lying on the main sequence.

The HR diagrams of globular clusters are known through

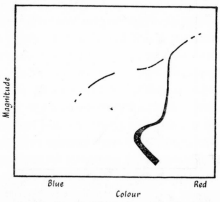

FIG. 54. Colour-magnitude diagram of a globular cluster. The most heavily populated branches in the diagram are drawn thickest.

studies of *colour* rather than spectra because of the faintness of the stars. They take the form of fig. 54. The heavy line at the bottom is thickly populated with stars, and coincides, at least roughly, with the ordinary main sequence. The characteristic bending upwards to the right, through sub-giants to red giants, is explained theoretically if (1) globular clusters are much older than most open clusters, (2) the stars are unmixed, (3) the metal/hydrogen abundance ratio is much smaller in the globular clusters.

[1] However, the spectra of T Tauri stars suggest outward motion rather than inward motion of gases at their surface.

Now we saw in the last chapter that there is indeed spectroscopic evidence that some globular clusters are extremely deficient in metals (compared with hydrogen) at least in their atmospheres. Further, we have found that there are stars outside globular clusters which share the same physical peculiarities (metal-weakness) and dynamical properties (high velocity relative to the Sun) with the globular clusters. We have good reason to suppose that these high-velocity objects are among the oldest in the Galaxy.

Why should metals be deficient compared with hydrogen in old stars when we would expect hydrogen deficiency to be a mark of old age? It is believed that the heavy elements are built up from the light ones, but this requires very much higher temperatures than those for the proton–proton reaction and carbon cycle. This process could certainly occur in supernova explosions and perhaps in some stellar interiors. If one makes the simplifying assumption that in its original state only hydrogen atoms were present in the universe and that heavier elements were gradually formed (and dissipated in interstellar space through supernova explosions), then stars born late in the history of the universe must be richer in metals compared with hydrogen than those formed early – some of which may survive as very old stars. We are sure that the luminous O and B stars are very young in the astronomical time-scale and that some star-formation must be going on even now. Perhaps the material from which these young stars are formed has previously existed in several successive generations of stars. If there has been a gradual building-up of heavy elements from primeval hydrogen, then a deficiency of metals in the oldest stars is to be expected. Differences in composition of the original matter from which stars are formed should be visible in their atmospheres if they are not subject to internal mixing, and perhaps even if they are mixed.

P

It has been mentioned that star-formation must be occurring even now. Where should we look for the birth of stars? It is believed that the birth occurs in the clouds of dust and gas that are found chiefly in spiral arms. Supporting evidence for this comes from the fact that the young O and B stars are also concentrated mostly within spiral arms. An O type star cannot live for more than 10 million years, and during this time it will only travel some 100 parsecs (at the average speed of an O type star), that is about 1 per cent of the distance of the Sun to the centre of the Galaxy. Most of the O type stars that we see in spiral arms must be astronomically rather close to their birth-place.

Stellar populations. When Baade resolved the nucleus of the Andromeda nebula into red stars, he recognized two types of stellar population. Population I includes bright O and B stars, open clusters, Cepheid variables, interstellar gas and other objects found in spiral arms, all strongly concentrated to the plane of the Milky Way. Population II includes the high-velocity objects with little or no concentration to the galactic plane (globular clusters, RR Lyrae variables, etc.).[1] Population I includes the youngest stars, Population II the oldest. Note that in Population I the brightest stars are blue, in Population II the brightest stars are red.

This concept has been very useful in stimulating profitable lines of research. At the same time the picture may have been oversimplified. Very probably intermediate types of population exist. For instance, a more elaborate scheme has been proposed in which as many as five Populations are recognized. In Baade's original scheme no distinction is drawn between the types of population found in the *nucleus* and in the *halo* surrounding the Galaxy. Besides the red stars in the nucleus of the Andromeda nebula, Baade recognized similar

[1] See fig. 25 (p. 97) where I and II refer to these two Population Types.

stars between the spiral arms. It is very difficult to recognize counterparts of this inter-arm population in our own Galaxy.

The relationship of the M type variables (among the reddest stars known) to the scheme of Populations needs clarifying. Those variables with periods greater than 200 days belong to Population I. Periods less than 200 days seem to be associated with Population II. No explanation for this is available.

Stellar populations can only be considered statistically, and it is often misleading to enquire whether a particular star belongs to some type of population or not. If the theory of stellar evolution can be established firmly, it may become possible to measure roughly the ages of individual stars. The scheme of population types may then simply become a matter of ordering stars into age-groups.

An important check on the theory of stellar evolution would be the measurement of masses of bright members of Baade's Population II. According to theory these stars must disobey the mass–luminosity relation very markedly in the sense of being over-luminous. For instance, the brightest stars in globular clusters are believed to have masses only slightly greater than that of the Sun and yet to be more than 200 times as luminous. To measure the mass without assuming a mass–luminosity relation, we have to rely on visual or spectroscopic binaries and unfortunately examples are not known among bright Population II giants. We have evidence of some sub-giants being over-luminous. The data concerning masses of Population I giants seem to suggest that they obey the mass–luminosity relation.

Clearly there are hosts of questions being asked, many of which can only be answered by intensive spectroscopic observations of carefully selected individual stars. Radial velocities and their variations, accurate spectral classifications, spectra of variables, and studies of spectroscopic peculiarities suggesting anomalous abundances are all needed for refined checks on our ideas about stellar evolution. Studies of double stars – and eclipsing variables in particular – might be most profitable in providing clues, for we still have no clear answer to the question of the origin of double or multiple stars, nor why there are so many of them. As to the origin of planetary systems we are still more in the dark.

Structure of the Galaxy. Great strides have been made in our understanding of the general structure of the Milky Way, and as we have seen a beginning has been made in roughly sketching out spiral arms. But it is to be hoped that the accuracy of spectroscopic measurements of distance will be greatly improved. The distance to the centre of the Galaxy is still only roughly known and we would like to know far more details about the rotation of the Galaxy. The persistence of spiral arms in a galaxy subject to differential rotation is un-explained. The apparent expansion of young clusters has stimulated spectroscopic determinations of radial velocities which should lead to a better understanding of this pheno-menon.

Problems of identification. The fundamental problem of identifying sources of stellar absorption and emission features which challenged spectroscopists of 100 years ago, is to a large extent solved. The two chief spectra awaiting identification now are the diffuse dark lines originating in interstellar space, and the bright bands of supernovae (Type I). Following the successes with the nebular and coronal lines, the solution of such residual problems ought not to be delayed much longer.

The accurate identification of numerous faint lines in the solar spectrum rests on the patient application of well-established principles. Here, and in the spectra of some of the coolest stars, laboratory investigation of some simple molecules is the primary need.

However, each new technique that extends the range of wavelengths observable by astrophysicists involves anew the problem of identification. The ultra-violet spectra of the Sun, recovered from high-altitude rockets, have already pioneered the region of Lyman α; much more intimate understanding of the physics of stellar atmospheres must follow on the application of this technique to stars. With the help of infrared receivers too we are learning more in this little explored region. But this work is hindered by absorption in the Earth's atmosphere, and again high-altitude spectroscopy is required.

Spectroscopic techniques. Many new laboratory techniques are being adapted to spectroscopic needs. The photo-electric cell in various forms may replace the photographic plate as a sensitive detector. For the purpose of recording wide ranges of wavelength *simultaneously* the photographic plate remains extremely efficient and convenient as a permanent record, although image tube converters may supplant it eventually. The photo-electric cell is best suited to accurate measurement of narrow stretches of the spectrum. Carefully chosen interference filters will isolate critical wavelengths, and when these regions are measured photo-electrically very accurate spectral classification becomes possible. As instrumental devices become more efficient the astronomer is continually faced with the problem of reducing vast quantities of observational data, and further devices are required to handle the data and interpret them. In the meantime we need more and more spectroscopic observations as interest in various astrophysical problems ebbs and flows through the decades. It is clearly better by intelligent selection to observe those objects of critical importance than to wait, like Mr Micawber, for something to turn up, although important discoveries are occasionally made by accident. In the meantime we can be sure that the long history of spectroscopic discoveries beginning with Newton's experiments on white light and Kirchhoff's experiments in the laboratory is very far from being ended.

Appendix I

IDENTIFICATIONS OF CHIEF
FRAUNHOFER LINES

Fraunhofer Designation	Wavelength (angstroms)	Identification
A	7594	O_2 band-head (terrestrial)
B	6867	O_2 band-head (terrestrial)
C	6563	$H\alpha$
D1	5896	Na
D2	5890	Na
E1	5270	Fe
E_b	5183–5168	Mg (triplet)
F	4861	$H\beta$
G	4308	CH + Fe
H	3968	Ca (ionized)
K	3933	Ca (ionized)

Appendix II

SELECTED LIST OF ASTRO-
PHYSICALLY IMPORTANT LINES

(a) λ > 2950 A

Resonance Lines

Atom	Wavelength	Atom	Wavelength
Li I	6707·7	Ca II	3933·7
	6707·9	Cr I	4254·3
Be II	3130·4	Mn I	4030·8
	3131·1	Fe I	3859·9
Na I	5890·0	Rb I	7800·2
	5895·9	Sr I	4607·3
Mg I	4571·1	Sr II	4077·7
Al I	3961·5	Y II	3633·1
K I	7664·9	In I	4511·3
K I	4044·1	Ba I	5535·5
Ca I	4226·7	Ba II	4554·0

Subordinate Lines

Atom	Wavelength	Excitation Potential (lower state)
H	6562·8	10·1
H	4861·3	10·1
H	4340·5	10·1
He I	5876·6 t	20·9
He I	4471·5 t	20·9
He I	3888·6	19·7
He II	4686·7	48·2
C II	4267·1 d	18·0
C III	4647·4	29·4
N II	3995·0	18·4
N III	4097·3	27·3

Subordinate Lines

Atom	Wavelength	Excitation Potential (lower state)
N III	4640·6	30·3
O II	4649·1	22·9
Mg I	5183·6	2·7
Mg II	4481·2 d	8·8
Si I	3905·5	1·9
Si II	4130·9	9·8
Si III	4552·7	18·9
Si IV	4088·9	23·9
Ca II	8542·1	1·7
Sc II	4246·8	0·3
Fe I	4383·5	1·5
Fe I	4045·8	1·5
Fe II	4233·2	2·6
Fe III	4419·6	8·2
Y II	4374·9	0·4

(b) λ < 2950 A

Atom	Wavelength (vacuum)	Atom	Wavelength (vacuum)
H	1215·7 d	O II	834·5
H	1025·7 d	O III	703·8
He I	584·3	Ne I	735·9
He II	303·8 d	Ne II	460·7
He II	256·3 d	Ne III	489·5
C II	1335·7 d	Mg I	2852·1*
C III	977·0	Mg II	2795·5*
N II	1085·7	Si II	1265·0
N III	991·6	Fe II	2599·4
O I	1302·2		

* Wavelength in air

d   close double
t   close triple

Appendix III

ASTROPHYSICALLY IMPORTANT

IONIZATION POTENTIALS

Atom	(I) Neutral I.P.	(II) Once Ionized I.P.	(III) Doubly Ionized I.P.
H	13·54	—	
He	24·48	54·17	
Li	5·37		
C	11·20	24·28	47·67
N	14·49	29·49	47·24
O	13·56	35·00	54·71
Ne	21·47	40·91	63·3
Na	5·12	47·10	
Mg	7·61	14·97	
Al	5·96	18·75	
Si	8·11	16·27	33·32
S	10·31	23·3	
Ar	15·69	27·5	
K	4·32	31·7	
Ca	6·09	11·82	
Ti	6·81	13·6	
Fe	7·86	16·16	30·48
Ni	7·61	18·4	
Sr	5·67	10·98	
Y	6·5	12·3	
Zr	6·92	13·97	
Cs	3·88		
Ba	5·19	9·96	
La	5·59	11·38	

Data quoted from C. E. Moore, Revised Multiplet Table (1945), *Contr. Princeton Obs.* no. 20, in which data for other ions will also be found.

Appendix IV

THE IONIZATION EQUATION

The relative concentration of neutral (X) and ionized (X^+) atoms, in a concentration of N_e electrons/cm³ at temperature T, is given by

$$\frac{X^+ . N_e}{X} = \frac{(2\pi mkT)}{h^3} . \frac{2B^+(T)}{B(T)} . e^{-I/kT}$$

where m is the mass of the electron, k is Boltzmann's constant, h is Planck's constant, $B(T)$ is the partition function describing how the atoms are distributed among the various possible energy levels (the $+$ sign referring to the similar function for the once ionized atoms). I is the ionization potential.

The electron pressure P_e is given by the equation

$$P_e = N_e kT$$

The most usual form in which the ionization equation is applied is

$$\log\left(\frac{X^+}{X}\right) = 2.5T - \frac{5040}{T} . I - \log P_e - 0.48 + \log\frac{2B^+(T)}{B(T)}$$

where T is in °K, I is in volts, and P_e in dynes/cm².

Nomograms for the calculation of the state of ionization in various conditions are given by A. Unsöld in *Physik der Sternatmospharen*, pp. 87, 88 (2nd Edition, 1955).

Appendix V

THE IDENTIFICATION OF BRIGHT
LINES IN THE CORONA[1]

The spectrum of 'coronium' was not observed in any source but the corona until 1933 when Adams and Joy found the bright red (6374 A) and green (5303) lines in the spectrum of the nova RS Ophiuchi. Subsequently the red line has been identified in other novae during declining light.

The next clue came in 1937 when Edlén and Swings found that some strong emission lines observed in Nova Pictoris (1925) some years after maximum could be identified with 'forbidden' lines of Fe VI and Fe VII. These ions had been investigated in the laboratory in the far ultra-violet and the identification depended on an analysis of the energy levels, just as in the identification of nebulium (p. 133).

In 1939 Grotrian pointed out that the wavelength of the red coronal line (6374 A) agreed reasonably with that predicted for a transition of [Fe X]; another coronal line could be similarly ascribed to [Fe XI]. Since highly ionized Fe and the coronal lines were both known to be associated with the late stages of novae, Grotrian's suggested identification was plausible.

Finally, in 1941, Edlén marshalled arguments in favour of identifying the great majority of the coronal lines. Only four lines ([Fe X] 6374, [Fe XI] 7892, [Ca XII] 3328, [Ca XIII] 4086) could be ascribed to transitions with wavelengths directly predicted from laboratory observations of permitted lines. The others could only be identified by studying *iso-electronic sequences*, that is, similar transitions in a sequence of successive elements in the Periodic Table increasingly ionized, so that each ion has the same number of residual electrons.

For example, take the best known coronal line, 5303 A, ascribed by Edlén to [Fe XIV]. With thirteen electrons removed, iron is reduced to 13 electrons and is therefore similar to neutral aluminium. We expect the Grotrian diagram of Fe XIV to be similar to that of Al I, but with

[1] It is recommended that this Appendix be read *after* Chapter 9 (Gaseous Nebulae).

236

a magnified scale, so that all the Fe XIV wavelengths are much shorter. The Grotrian diagram of Al I appears in fig. 55, restricted to the two well-known resonance lines at 3944, 3961. It is seen that within the double (ground) level a forbidden transition, shown by dots, might occur – in favourable circumstances.

SEPARATIONS $\Delta\nu$ OF THE GROUND LEVEL IN THE
ISO-ELECTRONIC SEQUENCE Al I TO Ni XVI

Atomic Number	Ion	$\Delta\nu$	$\sqrt[4]{\tfrac{2}{3}\Delta\nu}$	Difference
13	Al I	112·04	2·939	0·781
14	Si II	287·3	3·720	·675
15	P III	559·6	4·395	·622
16	S IV	950·2	5·017	·599
17	Cl V	1492	5·616	·579
18	Ar VI	2210	6·195	·564
19	K VII	3131	6·759	·560
20	Ca VIII	4305	7·319	·552
21	Sc IX	5759	7·871	
22	Ti X			
23	V XI			·543
24	Cr XII			
25	Mn XIII			
26	Fe XIV	18,852·5 (5303 A)	10·588	
27	Co XV			·538
28	Ni XVI	27,762 (3601 A)	11·664	

The wave-numbers in the third column are derived from laboratory observations from Al I to Sc IX; those quoted for Fe XIV and Ni XVI correspond to observed coronal lines.

Note the smooth run of the differences in the last column.

Data from Edlén, *Month. Not. Roy. Ast. Soc.* **105**, 325, 1945.

Laboratory observations give the separation $\Delta\nu$ of the ground level for all members of the iso-electronic sequence Al I, Si II, P III . . . to Sc IX. These are listed in the accompanying table, together with $\sqrt[4]{\tfrac{2}{3}\Delta\nu}$. This latter quantity is known to increase approximately linearly along an iso-electronic sequence. If the increase were exactly linear, the differences in the last column would be constant, and one could predict accurately wavelengths of the forbidden lines for ions in the sequence beyond Sc IX. However, the differences change fairly steadily along the sequence and the argument for identifying the line 5303 with [Fe XIV] becomes more indirect.

If 5303 is correctly identified with [Fe XIV] in this sequence, one finds that the average difference for the ions Sc IX to Fe XIV is 0·543. Then one can extrapolate the sequence accurately two places further and predict a wavelength of 3601 Å for the same transition in [Ni XVI]. There *is* another strong coronal line at 3601 A. We have thus good grounds for believing that the coronal lines 5303 and 3601 may belong to this particular iso-electronic sequence.

FIG. 55. Grotrian diagram of resonance lines of Al I.

Examination of other iso-electronic sequences leads to similar identifications of strong lines with highly ionized Fe, Ni, Ca and Ar. Altogether, Edlén found that iron and nickel (known to be the most abundant elements cosmically in the iron group) would account for 14 coronal lines contributing 95 per cent of the light in the line spectrum.

Strong confirmation of the whole scheme comes from the fact that Lyot had already classed coronal lines into four groups according to the manner in which they changed from day to day, and that in Edlén's scheme the lines in each of Lyot's groups had about the same ionization potential. It is the ionization potential that mainly determines the diurnal changes. This is very similar to the situation found in spectra of planetary nebulae, where the size of monochromatic images varies with ionization potential and gave Bowen a clue in his identification of the nebular lines.

The two conditions favourable to the appearance of forbidden lines are (1) low density, (2) low intensity of radiation (p. 136).

The density of the corona is certainly very low, but condition (2) seemed to argue strongly against the coronal spectrum consisting of forbidden lines. However, the condition refers to the *intensity of radiation to which the particular ion will respond*. Permitted lines of Fe XIV (ionization potential 355 volts) have wavelengths of only a few angstroms, in the region of soft X-rays. Unless the Sun's radiation departs wildly from that of a black body it must be very weak at such wavelengths, so that condition (2) can be fulfilled after all.

Appendix VI

HYDROGEN–HELIUM TRANSMUTA-

TIONS IN STELLAR INTERIORS

The building of helium from hydrogen must take place in a series of steps rather than the simultaneous fusion of four hydrogen atoms. The two recognized cycles are the proton–proton reaction and the carbon cycle. The individual steps are described below in the usual symbolic form, in which the superscripts to the chemical symbols give the weights of the various isotopes, e^+ stands for a positive electron, ν for a neutrino, γ for γ-rays.

Proton–Proton reaction.

$$H^1 + H^1 \longrightarrow H^2 + e^+ + \nu$$
$$H^2 + H^1 \longrightarrow He^3 + \gamma$$
$$He^3 + He^3 \longrightarrow He^4 + H^1 + H^1$$

The middle step takes place practically instantaneously as compared with the other two. Since the last step requires two He^3 isotopes, the first two steps must each take place twice for the building of one He^4 nucleus.

Carbon cycle.

$$C^{12} + H^1 \longrightarrow N^{13} + \gamma$$
$$N^{13} \longrightarrow C^{13} + e^+ + \nu$$
$$C^{13} + H^1 \longrightarrow N^{14} + \gamma$$
$$N^{14} + H^1 \longrightarrow O^{15} + \gamma$$
$$O^{15} \longrightarrow N^{15} + e^+ + \nu$$
$$N^{15} + H^1 \longrightarrow C^{12} + He^4$$

The decay of N^{13} and O^{15} in the second and fifth steps takes place very quickly. The great interest of the cycle is that the final step reproduces the C^{12} which was used up in the first step. The He^4 nucleus that finally appears has thus been built up from four hydrogen atoms, with carbon, nitrogen and oxygen acting only as catalysts.

A minor point is that the last step can sometimes, but relatively rarely, produce O^{16} instead of C^{12} and He^4. This means that long-term operation of the carbon cycle should involve some build-up of oxygen at the expense of carbon.

It will be noticed that the proton–proton reaction does not require the original presence of any element but hydrogen.

Note that in all the above transmutations the usual rules are observed that

(1) the isotopic numbers (superscripts) total the same before and after the transmutation,

(2) the total nuclear charges (or the sum of atomic numbers) remain unchanged unless a positive electron is emitted, when they are reduced by one.

For other nuclear reactions which may be important in stellar interiors, see G. R. and E. M. Burbidge, *Encyclopaedia of Physics*, LI, 134, 1958.

BIBLIOGRAPHY

B = book   T = tables of observational data, etc.
P = original paper   A = illustrative atlas

GENERAL

L. GOLDBERG and L. H. ALLER. *Atoms, Stars and Nebulae.*
Blakiston Press and John Churchill, 1943.   (B)

H. N. RUSSELL, R. S. DUGAN and J. Q. STEWART. *Astronomy*, Vol. II.
Ginn and Co. Revised Edition, 1927.   (B)
(The standard textbook on astrophysics which is still indispensable
despite its omission of the latest developments.)

W. H. McCREA. *Physics of the Sun and Stars.* Hutchinson, 1950.   (B)
(A very useful introduction to astrophysical theory in simple terms.)

S. FLÜGGE, ed. *Encyclopedia of Physics*, L to LIII. Springer, 1958. (B)
(Advanced and up-to-date information on all branches of astrophysics.)

V. A. AMBARTSUMYAN. *Theoretical Astrophysics.* Pergamon Press,
1958 (translated from the Russian by J. B. Sykes.)   (B)

L. H. ALLER. *Astrophysics* (2 vols.). Ronald Press, 1953.   (B)

CHAPTER 2

E. C. C. BALY. *Spectroscopy* (4 vols.). Longmans, 1929.   (B)

R. A. SAWYER. *Experimental Spectroscopy.* Prentice-Hall, 1944. (B)

A. BEER, ed. *Vistas in Astronomy.* Pergamon Press, 1956.
    p. 400   I. S. Bowen. Astronomical spectrographs: past, present and
             future.
    p. 1223 Th. Dunham, Jr. Methods in stellar spectroscopy.

CHAPTER 3

A. C. CANDLER. *Atomic Spectra* (2 vols.). Cambridge U.P., 1937. (B)

H. E. WHITE. *Introduction to Atomic Spectra.* McGraw-Hill, 1934. (B)

W. GROTRIAN. *Handbuch der Astrophysik*, III/2, 475 (Grotrian diagrams). Springer, 1930.   (A)

P. W. MERRILL. *Lines of the Chemical Elements in Astronomical Spectra.*
Carnegie Inst. Washington, Publ. 610, 1956.   (AT)

C. E. MOORE. *Revised Multiplet Table.* Princeton Obs. Contrib. no. 20,
1945.   (T)

CHAPTER 4

Stellar Temperature Scale:

G. P. KUIPER. The stellar temperature scale. *Ap. J.*, **88**, 429, 1938. (P

R. M. PETRIE. Absorption line intensities, spectral classification and excitation temperatures for the O stars. *Publ. D.A.O.*, **VII**, 321, 1947. (P)

MKK Classification:

W. W. MORGAN, P. C. KEENAN and E. KELLMANN. *An atlas of stellar spectra*. Chicago U.P., 1943. (A)

MK Standard Stars:

W. W. MORGAN and H. L. JOHNSON. Fundamental stellar photometry for standards of spectral type on the revised system of the Yerkes Spectral Atlas. *Ap. J.*, **117**, 313, 1953. (P)

CHAPTER 5

Ionization Theory: see general references above.

Excitation Temperatures, etc.:

W. S. ADAMS and H. N. RUSSELL. Preliminary results of a new method for the analysis of stellar spectra. *Ap. J.*, **68**, 9, 1928. (P)

K. O. WRIGHT. A study of line intensities in the spectra of four solar type stars. *Publ. D.A.O.*, **VIII**, 1, 1947. (P)

CHAPTER 6

R. E. WILSON. *General Catalogue of Radial Velocities*. Carnegie Inst. Washington, Publ. 601, 1953. (T)

Galactic Rotation:

J. S. PLASKETT and J. A. PEARCE. The motions of the O and B type stars and the scale of the Galaxy. *Publ. D.A.O.*, V, 241, 1936. (P)

M. W. FEAST and A. D. THACKERAY. Analysis of radial velocities of distant B type stars. *M.N.*, **118**, 125, 1958. (P)

Objective Prism Radial Velocities:

CH. FEHRENBACH *et al. Ann. d'Ap.*, **10**, 257, 306, 1947; *Journ. des Observateurs*, 1955–1958. (P)

CHAPTER 7

Revised Rowland Catalogue. Carnegie Inst. Washington, Publ. 386, 1928. (T)

M. MINNAERT, G. F. W. MULDERS and J. HOUTGAST. *Photometric Atlas of the Solar Spectrum*. Utrecht, 1940. (A)

Granulation:

R. S. RICHARDSON and M. SCHWARZSCHILD. On the turbulent velocities of solar granules. *Ap. J.*, **111**, 351, 1950. (P)

Sunspot Spectrum Analysis:

C. E. MOORE. Some results from a study of the atomic lines in the sunspot spectrum. *Ap. J.*, **75**, 222, 298, 1932. (P)

Wavelengths and Relativity Shift:

M. G. ADAM. Interferometric measurements of wavelengths. *M.N.*, **118**, 106, 1958 (and preceding papers). (P)

General:

G. ABETTI. *Solar Research*. Eyre and Spottiswoode. (In preparation.) (B)

Solar Atmosphere and Corona:

C. DE JAGER. The structure and dynamics of the solar atmosphere. *Encyclopedia of Physics*, **LII**, 80, 1958. (BP)

B. EDLÉN. The identification of the coronal lines. *M.N.*, **105**, 325, 1946. (P)

Planetary Atmospheres:

G. P. KUIPER, ed. *Atmospheres of the Earth and Planets*. Chicago U.P., 1948. (B)

H. C. UREY. The atmospheres of the planets. *Encyclopedia of Physics*, **LII**, 363, 1958. (BP)

Comets:

P. SWINGS. The spectra of the comets. *Vistas in Astronomy*. Ed. A. Beer, p. 958, 1956. (BP)

P. SWINGS and L. HASER. *Atlas of Representative Cometary Spectra*. University of Liége, Institut d'Astrophysique, 1956. (A)

CHAPTER 8

R. G. AITKEN. *The Binary Stars*. McGraw-Hill, 1935. (B)

Mass-Luminosity Relation:

G. P. KUIPER. The empirical mass-luminosity relation. *Ap. J.*, **88**, 472, 1938. (P)

A. S. EDDINGTON. *Internal Constitution of the Stars*. Cambridge U.P., 1926. (B)

O. STRUVE. *Stellar Evolution*. Princeton U.P., 1950. (B)

CHAPTER 9

L. H. ALLER. *Gaseous Nebulae.* Chapman and Hall, 1956. (B)

JEAN DUFAY. *Galactic Nebulae and Interstellar Matter* (translated from the French by A. J. Pomerans). Hutchinson, 1957. (B)

Identification of nebular lines:

    I. S. BOWEN. The origin of the nebular lines and the structure of the planetary nebulae. *Ap. J.*, **67**, 1, 1928. (P)

Fluorescence:

    I. S. BOWEN. The spectra and composition of the planetary nebulae. *Ap. J.*, **81**, 1, 1935. (P)

CHAPTER 10

J. L. GREENSTEIN. Interstellar Matter. *Astrophysics*, p. 526 (ed. J. A. Hynek). McGraw-Hill, 1951. (BP)

Molecular Lines:

    A. MCKELLAR. Molecular lines from the lowest states of diatomic molecules composed of atoms probably present in interstellar space. *Publ. D.A.O.*, **VII**, 251, 1941. (P)

Interstellar Hydrogen:

    B. STRÖMGREN. The physical state of interstellar hydrogen. *Ap. J.*, **89**, 526, 1939. (P)

CHAPTER 11

C. PAYNE-GAPOSCHKIN. *The Galactic Novae.* North-Holland Publishing Co., 1957. (B)

Spectra of Novae:

    D. B. MCLAUGHLIN. Spectral Stages of Novae. *Ap. J.*, **95**, 428, 1942. (P)

    F. J. M. STRATTON and W. H. MANNING. *Atlas of Spectra of Nova Herculis, 1934.* Solar Physics Observatory, Cambridge, 1939. (A)

    F. ZWICKY. Supernovae. *Encyclopedia of Physics*, **LI**, 779. 1958. (BP)

P Cygni Stars:

    C. S. BEALS. The spectra of P Cygni Stars. *Publ. D.A.O.*, **IX**, 1, 1950. (P)

Variable Stars:

    P. W. MERRILL. *Spectra of Long-Period Variable Stars.* Chicago U.P., 1940. (B)

    A. H. JOY. Spectroscopic Observations of Mira Ceti, 1934–1952. *Ap. J.* (Suppt.), **I**, 39, 1954. (P)

    H. ABT. An analysis of W Virginis. *Ap. J.* (Suppt.), **I**, 63, 1954. (P)

CHAPTER 12

Calibration of MK spectra:

W. W. MORGAN and P. C. KEENAN. *Astrophysics*, p. 12. ed. J. A. Hynek, McGraw-Hill, 1950. (BP)

Pulsation Parallaxes:

P. LEDOUX and TH. WALRAVEN. *Encyclopedia of Physics*, **LI**, 594, 1958. (BP)

Calcium Emission:

O. C. WILSON and M. K. V. BAPPU. H and K emission in late-type stars. *Ap. J.*, **125**, 161, 1957. (P)

CHAPTER 13

E. P. HUBBLE. *The Realm of the Nebulae*. Yale U.P., 1936. (B)
E. LINDSAY. *Galaxies*. Eyre and Spottiswoode. (In preparation.) (B)

Spectra of Galaxies:

W. W. MORGAN and N. U. MAYALL. A spectral classification of galaxies. *P.A.S.P.*, **69**, 291, 1957. (P)
W. W. MORGAN. A preliminary classification of the forms of galaxies according to their stellar populations. *P.A.S.P.*, **70**, 364, 1958. (P)

Distances of Galaxies:

A. R. SANDAGE. Current problems in the extragalactic distance scale. *Ap. J.*, **127**, 513, 1958. (P)

Velocities of Galaxies:

M. L. HUMASON, N. U. MAYALL and A. R. SANDAGE. Redshifts and magnitudes of extragalactic nebulae. *Ap. J.*, **61**, 97. (P)

CHAPTER 14

A. UNSOLD. *Physik der Sternatmosphären* (2nd Edition, 1955). Springer. (B)
C. W. ALLEN. *Astrophysical Quantities*. Athlone Press, 1955 (see pp. 63–78 for oscillator strengths). (B)

Magnetic Stars:

H. W. BABCOCK. A catalog of magnetic stars. *Ap. J.* (Suppt.), **III**, 141, 1958. (P)
H. W. BABCOCK and T. G. COWLING. General magnetic fields in the Sun and stars. *M.N.*, **113**, 357, 1953. (P)
A. J. DEUTSCH. *Encyclopedia of Physics*, **LI**, 689.

CHAPTER 15

H. N. RUSSELL. On the composition of the Sun's atmosphere. *Ap. J.*, **70**, 11, 1929. (P)

M. G. J. MINNAERT. The determination of cosmic abundances. *M.N.*, **117**, 315, 1957. (P)

P. C. KEENAN. Stars with peculiar spectra. *Encyclopedia of Physics*, **L**, 93. (BP)

P. W. MERRILL and C. G. BURWELL. Mt. Wilson catalogue and bibliography of stars of classes B and A whose spectra have bright hydrogen lines. *Ap. J.*, **78**, 87, 1933; *Ap. J.*, **98**, 153, 1943; *Ap. J.*, **110**, 387, 1949. (T)

W. P. BIDELMAN. Catalogue and bibliography of emission line stars of types later than B. *Ap. J.* (Suppt.), **1**, 175, 1954. (T)

CHAPTER 16

D. J. K. O'CONNELL, ed. *Stellar Populations*. Richerche Astronomiche, **5**. Vatican, 1958. (BP)

M. SCHWARZSCHILD. *Structure and Evolution of the Stars*. Princeton U.P., 1958. (B)

GLOSSARY OF TERMS

Absolute temperature. Temperature measured on the centigrade scale but having zero at $-273°\cdot2$ C, i.e. the ideal absolute zero at which molecules would have no kinetic energy. Designated °K, after Kelvin.

Albedo. The reflecting power of a body, defined as the ratio of the intensities of the reflected and incident light.

Angstrom unit (A). $1 A = 10^{-8}$ cm. The unit of wavelength of light. Visible light extends from wavelengths of about 3900 A (violet) to 7000 A (deep red).

Astronomical Unit. The unit of astronomical distance within the solar system, defined as the semi-major axis of the Earth's orbit around the Sun. 1 astronomical unit = $93\cdot0$ million miles (Spencer Jones, 1942) = $1\cdot494 \times 10^{13}$ cm. 1 parsec (*q.v.*) = 206,265 astronomical units.

Atmosphere (as unit of pressure). 1 atmosphere = $1\cdot013 \times 10^6$ dynes/cm².

BD. Abbreviation for Bonner Durchmusterung, an early catalogue of stars down to about 9th magnitude covering the northern parts of the sky. Catalogued stars are designated by BD followed by the star's declination and its serial number in that zone of declination.

Black body. An ideal substance which will absorb all radiation falling on it, and which would thus appear blacker than any actual substance when cold. It would also appear brighter, for its temperature, than any actual substance when hot.

Bolometer. An instrument for measuring the total radiant energy (including that of invisible heat rays) of a body.

The *bolometric magnitude* of a star is a measure of the total radiant energy (including ultra-violet radiation blocked by the Earth's atmosphere) of the star on the same scale as visual magnitudes. The correction required to correct visual magnitudes into bolometric is the *bolometric correction*; it is largest for the hottest and coolest stars most of whose radiation is invisible.

Coelostat. A mechanical arrangement of mirrors (usually two) whereby the reflected light of stars or the Sun is kept stationary as the Earth rotates.

Dispersion (angular, linear). Light of different wavelengths λ is deviated by a prism or grating through different angles θ. The rate of change of θ with λ, $d\theta/d\lambda$, is the *angular dispersion*. If the deviated light is brought to a focus by a camera of focal length f, the *linear dispersion*, $f\,d\theta/d\lambda$, measures the scale of the focused spectrum. The reciprocal of this, expressed in A/mm, is commonly used as a measure of the dispersion.

Distance modulus. A convenient measure of astronomical distances in stellar magnitudes. It is the difference between a star's actual apparent magnitude m and the magnitude M that it would have if placed at the standard distance of 10 parsecs (absolute magnitude).

Electron temperature. The temperature which describes the various velocities of electrons in a gas according to Maxwell's law (see also Kinetic temperature).

Gauss. The c.g.s. unit of magnetic force (alternatively but more rarely called *oersted*).

HD number. The number of a star in the Henry Draper Catalogue; very frequently used in astronomical literature.

HR diagram. The Hertzsprung–Russell diagram in which a star's absolute magnitude is plotted against its spectral type.

Instrumental errors. Errors of observation which originate solely in the instruments used.

Interferometer. An instrument, taking a variety of forms, which makes use of the properties of interfering light-waves for various purposes. In the laboratory it is useful for very accurate measures of wavelength or for testing optical parts. Examples of astronomical uses are the measurement of diameters of some exceptionally large stars and the study of motions of gases in nebulae.

Ionization potential. The energy required to remove an electron from an atom (first I.P.). When the atom has already lost one, two or more electrons, the energy required to remove the next is known as the second, third, etc., ionization potential. Usually measured in electron-volts.

Isotopes. Atoms having the same number of outer electrons (and therefore the same chemical properties) but different atomic weights (as a result of different numbers of neutrons in the nucleus).

$°K$. See Absolute temperature.

Kinetic energy. The energy possessed by a body of mass m by virtue of its motion (with velocity v). Mathematically $\frac{1}{2}mv^2$.

Kinetic temperature. The temperature of a gas measured by the average kinetic energy of its constituent particles. For a monatomic gas composed of atoms all of the same mass m moving with average velocity v, the kinetic temperature T is defined by the Maxwell relation $\frac{1}{2}mv^2 = \frac{3}{2}RT$, where $R = 1\cdot38 \times 10^{-16}$ ergs/deg (Boltzmann's constant). (See J. H. Jeans, *An Introduction to the Kinetic Theory of Gases*, Cambridge University Press, 1940.)

Luminosity. The total energy radiated per second by a star. According to Stefan's law the luminosity $L = 4\pi a R^2 T_e^4$ where $a = 5\cdot67 \times 10^{-5}$ ergs/cm²/deg⁴/sec (Stefan's constant) and T_e is known as the *effective temperature* (corresponding to the temperature near the surface of the star).

MK system. The Morgan–Keenan system of classifying stellar spectra.

Magnitude. A measure of a star's brightness on a logarithmic scale such that an increase of m magnitudes corresponds to a decrease in brightness I given by $m = -2\cdot5 \log I$ (e.g. a star of magnitude $1\cdot0$ appears 100 times as bright as a star of magnitude $6\cdot0$).

The range of colours contributing to the measured brightness must be specified, e.g. we have visual and photographic magnitudes (or bolometric magnitudes corresponding to all colours).

Megaparsec. One million parsecs. Unit of astronomical distance used for distances of spiral nebulae.

Minimum deviation. To produce the best results a prism is set at *minimum deviation* for wavelength λ, when light of that wavelength is least deviated from its original direction by the prism. For a prism of angle A and with refractive index n, the angle of minimum deviation θ is given by the equation

$$\sin\frac{A + \theta}{2} = n\sin\frac{A}{2}.$$

Objective prism. A prism placed in front of the objective of a telescope and used without slit or collimating lens.

Parallax. A measure of a star's distance. The angle subtended at the star by the Earth's mean distance from the Sun. The *trigonometrical parallax* is a direct measure of this angle by means of the Earth's orbital motion. A *spectroscopic parallax* is a deduced value of this angle from a spectroscopic estimate of the star's absolute magnitude M and its apparent magnitude m. The relation is

$$M - m = 5 + 5\log p$$
$$= 5 - 5\log r$$

where p is the parallax (in seconds of arc) and r is the distance in parsecs.

Parsec. Unit of astronomical distance. 1 parsec $= 3\cdot26$ light-years $= 3\cdot08 \times 10^{18}$ cm.

Partition function. The function (of temperature) which describes the distribution of atoms in various excited levels. (See reference in Appendix IV.)

Periastron. The point of nearest approach of a body (planet or another star) in its orbit around a star.

Photometry. The science of measuring the intensity of light by means of photography, photo-electric cell, etc.

Proper motion. The rate of change of position in the sky of a star, etc., relative to some frame of reference, in the first instance the background of fainter, more distant, stars. Usually measured in seconds of arc per annum or century.

Quantum of radiation. In Planck's Quantum Theory light is radiated in packets or *quanta* of energy, not continuously. The energy E of each quantum is given by $E = h\nu$, where ν is the frequency of radiation and $h = 6 \cdot 62 \times 10^{-27}$ ergs sec (Planck's constant).

Resonance lines. Lines in the spectrum of an atom or ion which require the least energy to excite them.

Resolving power. The power of a spectroscope to separate two closely adjacent lines (or in the case of a telescope to separate closely adjacent stars). If $d\lambda$ is the smallest possible spectroscopic separation at wavelength λ, the resolving power is defined as $\lambda/d\lambda$.

Schmidt telescope. A reflecting telescope giving a much wider field of good definition than an ordinary parabolic reflector on account of its using a spherical mirror in conjunction with a thin correcting plate.

Statistical weight. A measure of the probability of an atom being found in a particular energy level, apart from factors involving temperature. If J is the inner quantum number of a level, $2J + 1$ is its statistical weight.

Synchrotron radiation. The continuous radiation emitted by an electron when accelerated in a magnetic field. (Observed in the laboratory with an accelerator known as a synchrotron.)

Ultimate lines. The last lines to disappear in the spectrum of an element when the quantity of the element is diminished indefinitely.

Wavelength. The distance between successive crests of waves of light, measured usually in angstrom units (*q.v.*). A measure of pure colour.

Wave-number. The reciprocal of the wavelength, measured in cm^{-1}.

TABLE OF ELEMENTS AND ABBREVIATIONS

The list of elements is separated into groups, each ending with an inert gas having a complete shell of electrons.

Atomic Number	Element	Symbol	Atomic Number	Element	Symbol
1	Hydrogen	H	27	Cobalt	Co
2	Helium	He	28	Nickel	Ni
			29	Copper	Cu
3	Lithium	Li	30	Zinc	Zn
4	Beryllium	Be	31	Gallium	Ga
5	Boron	B	32	Germanium	Ge
6	Carbon	C	33	Arsenic	As
7	Nitrogen	N	34	Selenium	Se
8	Oxygen	O	35	Bromine	Br
9	Fluorine	F	36	Krypton	Kr
10	Neon	Ne			
			37	Rubidium	Rb
11	Sodium	Na	38	Strontium	Sr
12	Magnesium	Mg	39	Yttrium	Y
13	Aluminium	Al	40	Zirconium	Zr
14	Silicon	Si	41	Niobium	Nb
15	Phosphorus	P		(or Columbium)	(Cb)
16	Sulphur	S	42	Molybdenum	Mo
17	Chlorine	Cl	43	Technetium	Tc
18	Argon	Ar	44	Ruthenium	Ru
			45	Rhodium	Rh
19	Potassium	K	46	Palladium	Pd
20	Calcium	Ca	47	Silver	Ag
21	Scandium	Sc	48	Cadmium	Cd
22	Titanium	Ti	49	Indium	In
23	Vanadium	V	50	Tin	Sn
24	Chromium	Cr	51	Antimony	Sb
25	Manganese	Mn	52	Tellurium	Te
26	Iron	Fe	53	Iodine	I

Atomic Number	Element	Symbol	Atomic Number	Element	Symbol
54	Xenon	Xe	80	Mercury	Hg
			81	Thallium	Tl
55	Caesium	Cs	82	Lead	Pb
56	Barium	Ba	83	Bismuth	Bi
57	Lanthanum	La	84	Polonium	Po
58	Cerium	Ce	85	Astatine	At
59	Praseodymium	Pr	86	Radon	Rn
60	Neodymium	Nd			
61	Promethium	Pm	87	Francium	Fr
62	Samarium	Sm	88	Radium	Ra
63	Europium	Eu	89	Actinium	Ac
64	Gadolinium	Gd	90	Thorium	Th
65	Terbium	Tb	91	Protoactinium	Pa
66	Dysprosium	Dy	92	Uranium	U
67	Holmium	Ho			
68	Erbium	Er		*Artificial*	
69	Thulium	Tm		*Elements*	
70	Ytterbium	Yb	93	Neptunium	Np
71	Lutecium	Lu	94	Plutonium	Pu
72	Hafnium	Hf	95	Americium	Am
73	Tantalum	Ta	96	Curium	Cm
74	Tungsten	W	97	Berkelium	Bk
75	Rhenium	Re	98	Californium	Cf
76	Osmium	Os	99	Einsteinium	Es
77	Iridium	Ir	100	Fermium	Fm
78	Platinum	Pt	101	Mendelevium	Md
79	Gold	Au	102	Nobelium	No

INDEX